Frank Frankfort |

The Lighter Side of English Life

outlook

Frank Frankfort Moore

The Lighter Side of English Life

1st Edition | ISBN: 978-3-75242-025-8

Place of Publication: Frankfurt am Main, Germany

Year of Publication: 2020

Outlook Verlag GmbH, Germany.

THE LIGHTER SIDE OF ENGLISH LIFE

By Frank Frankfort Moore

CHAPTER ONE—THE VILLAGE

ONE MORNING A FEW MONTHS AGO A foreigner under the influence of an aeroplane descended somewhat hurriedly in a broad and—as he ascertained—a soft meadow in Nethershire; and while he was picking up his matches preparatory to lighting his cigarette—he has always a cigarette in his waistcoat pocket, for a man with a Kodak may be lurking behind the nearest tree—an agricultural labourer on his way to his work looked over the hedge at him. The foreign person noticed him, and after trying him in vain with German, French, and Hungarian, fell back upon English, and in the few words of that language which he knew, inquired the name of the place. "Why, Bleybar Lane, to be sure," replied the man, perceiving the trend of the question with the quick intelligence of the agricultural labourer; and when the stranger shook his head and lapsed into Russian, begging him to be more precise (for the aviator had not altogether recovered from the daze of his sudden arrival), the man repeated the words in a louder tone, "Bleybar Lane —everybody knows Bleybar Lane; and that's Thurswell that you can't see, beyond the windmill," and then walked on. Happily our parson, who had watched the descent of the stranger and was hastening to try if he could be of any help to him, came up at that moment and explained that he was in England, where English was, up to that time at least, spoken in preference to German or, indeed, any other language, and that breakfast would be ready at the Rectory in an hour.

I—THE ABORIGINES

It was the Rector who told me the story, adding in regard to the labourer —— "Isn't that just like Thurswell—fancying that a Czech who had just crossed the Channel, and believed himself to be in Belgium, should know all about Thurswell and its Bleybar Lane?"

I thought that it was very like Thurswell indeed, and afterwards I made it still more like by talking to the agricultural labourer himself about the incident.

"Ay, he spoke gibberish with a foreign accent, and I told him plain enough, when he had swept his arms and cried 'Where?' or words to that effect, that he was by Bleybar Lane, and that the place he couldn't see for the windmill was Thurswell; but it were no use: foreigners be in the main woeful ignorant for Christian persons, and I could see that he had no knowledge even of Thurswell when he heard the name."

"FOREIGNERS BE IN THE MAIN WOEFUL IGNORANT"

That is our village down to the ground. You could not persuade one of the aborigines that there is any place in England or outside it of greater importance than Thurswell, because there is no place of greater importance to the Thurswellian. An aged inhabitant was taken by his son to see the coronation procession, and when he was asked what it was like, replied, after a suitable pause, that it ran Thurs-well's Day very hard—Thurswell's Day is the name given to the First Sunday after Trinity, when the Free Foresters and Ancient Shepherds march to church in sashes, with a band made up of a fife, three flutes, a drum, a concertina, and a melodion.

"Ay, neighbours, it ran Thurswell's Day hard," he affirmed, and did not flinch from his statement in spite of the incredulous murmur that arose from the bench nearest the door, which was immediately suppressed by the landlord, who was apprehensive of a riot.

Thurswell is a village of antiquity. Its name occurs in *Domesday Book*, where you may look in vain for any mention of Brindlington, that mushroom town of 60.000 inhabitants, which is nine miles to the north, or even of

Broadminster, the Cathedral town, which is seven miles to the west. "Broadminster is where the Dean lives," I was told by the landlord of the Wheatsheaf at Thurswell when I was making inquiries about the district, "and Brindlington is where the brewery is; but my father got his ale at Pipstone, and I get mine there too, though it's a blow to Brindlington, for in harvest the best part of a cask goes within a week."

There are several other villages within a mile or so of Thurswell, and the inhabitants of some are infatuated enough to believe that they are on a social, as well as a commercial, level with the people of Thurswell. This singular hallucination caused a good deal of friction on all sides in years gone by, and *the rapprochement* that was eventually brought about between Thurswell and its neighbours by the thoughtfulness of a Rector, who preached a sermon on the vision of St. Peter and enjoined upon his hearers to remember that even though people have not been born in Thurswell they are still God's creatures, was a purely sentimental one, and did not last.

Some years ago an article appeared in the *Topographical Gazette* from the pen of an eminent archaeologist affirming that Thurswell must originally have been Thor's Well, so that the place dated back to the time of the worship of the Scandinavian god Thor; but while this evidence of its antiquity was received by some of us with enthusiasm—having been a resident in the village for a whole year I was naturally an ardent Thurswellian—it was, when reproduced in the *East Nethershire Weekly*, generally regarded as the invention of some one anxious to give the enemies of the village some ground for their animosity toward it. For the suggestion that it had a heathen origin was not one, it was felt, to which its people could tamely submit. There was some talk of a public meeting to protest against the conclusions come to by the archaeologist, and the Rector was considered in some quarters to be but a half-hearted champion of the Faith when he refused to lend the schoolhouse— sixty people could be crowded into it—for this purpose, his argument that the more heathen Thurswell had been in the past, the more marked should be its display of the Christian virtue of charity in the present, being criticised as savouring of Jesuitry. For months the matter was the leading topic of the neighbourhood, and the Hearts of Oak Habitation of the Ancient Shepherds drew up a resolution protesting in this connection against "archaeology and every form of idolatry." It was the misprint in the *Gazette* that changed "Hearts of Oak" into "Heads of Oak" in publishing the proceedings that quenched the violence of the discussion, and now it is considered bad taste to refer to it at all.

I. —THE CENTENARIANS

More recently still another busybody endeavoured to deprive the village of the reputation which it had long enjoyed as the centre of English longevity. Now it would be impossible for any one to study the dates on the tombstones in the churchyard without noticing how great was the number of centenarians who died within the first fifty years of the nineteenth century in the parish of Thurswell. There were apparently eighteen men and fourteen women interred after passing their hundredth year; indeed, one woman was recorded to have reached her hundred and twenty-seventh year, which is a good age for a woman. The people were naturally very proud of the constant references made in print to their longevity; but one day there came down to the village a member of the Statistical Society, and after busying himself among the musty parish registers for a month, he announced his discovery that in every case but one the date of the birth of the alleged centenarians was the date of the birth of their parents. The investigator had noticed that all the alleged centenarians had "departed this life" during the rectorship of the Rev. Thomas Ticehurst, and centenarianism had always been his fad. He had preached sermon after sermon on Methuselah and other distinguished multi-centenarians, and he spent his time travelling about the country in search of evidence in confirmation of the theory that Methuselah, though somewhat beyond the average in respect of age, might yet have been exceeded on his own ground by many people living in the country districts of England. Nothing was easier, the investigator tried to show, than for a clergyman in charge of the registers, who had such a hobby, to assume, when any very old man or woman died in his parish, that he or she actually was twenty years or so older; and as the Christian names were nearly always hereditary, in nine cases out of ten he accepted the registry of the birth of the father as that of the lately deceased man, and the date of the birth of the mother in regard to the aged woman, the result being a series of the most interesting inscriptions.

I must confess that I myself felt that I had a personal grievance against this busybody statistician. There is nothing so comforting to the middle-aged as a stroll through a cemetery of centenarians; and I had the most uncharitable feelings against the person who could make such an attempt to deprive me of the pleasant hope of living another sixty or seventy years.

But while we were still talking about the danger of permitting strangers to have access to the registers, I was told one morning that a man who had once been the gardener at the place which I had just acquired would like to see me. Now, I had had already some traffic with the superannuated gardener of my predecessor, and so I was now surprised to find myself face to face with quite a different person.

"You were not the gardener here," I said. "I saw him; his name is Craggs, and he still lives in the hollow."

"Oh ay, Jonas Craggs—young Joe, we called him; I knew his father," replied my visitor. "He was only here a matter of six-and-thirty years. I was superann'ated to make way for him. Young-Joe, we called him, and I was curious to see how things had come on in the garden of late."

"You were superannuated thirty-six years ago," said I. "What age are you now?"

"I'm ninety-eight, sir," he replied with a smirk.

"I'M NINETY-EIGHT, SIR"

I showed him round the garden. He said he could see that the things he had planted had grown summut; and I walked through the churchyard the next Sunday with the greatest complacency.

When I told the Rector that my experience of this grand old gardener tended to make me take the side of Thurswell and the neighbourhood against scientific investigation in regard to longevity, he assured me that if I paid a visit to a certain elderly lady who lived with a middle-aged granddaughter in a cottage on the road to Cransdown I should find ample confirmation of the faith for which I had a leaning. The lady's name was, he said, Martha Trendall, and she really was, he thought, a genuine centenarian, for she had a vivid recollection of events which had happened quite ninety years ago; and, unlike most reputed centenarians, she remembered many details of the historical incidents that had taken place in her young days; she was a most intelligent person altogether, and had evidently been at one time a great reader, though latterly her eyesight had shown signs of failing.

I made up my mind to pay a visit to this Mrs. Trendall, and thought that perhaps I might get material for a letter to the *Times* that should not leave the scientific investigator a leg to stand on. A month, however, elapsed before I carried out my intention, though the Rector thought this was not a case for procrastination: when a lady is anything over a hundred her hold upon life shows a tendency to relax, he said, for even the most notorious centenarians cannot be expected to live for ever. But when I managed to make my call I must confess that I was amply repaid for the time I spent in the company of Mrs. Trendall.

I found her sitting in her chair in what is called the chimney corner when it exists in its original condition in a cottage, but is termed the "ingle nook" in those red brick imitation cottages which are being flung about the country by those architects who concern themselves in the development of estates. I saw at once that such a figure would be out of place anywhere except in the chimney corner of a cottage kitchen, with immovable windows, but a "practicable" iron crane for the swinging of pots over the hearth fire. The atmosphere—thanks to the immobile casements—was also all that it should be: it was congenially centenarian, I perceived in a moment. It had a pleasant pungency of old bacon, but though I looked about for a genuine flitch maturing in the smoke, I failed to see one—still, the nail on which it should be hanging was there all right.

The old woman was quite alert. There was nothing of the wheezy gammer about her. Only one ear was slightly deaf, she told me when I had been introduced by her granddaughter—a woman certainly over fifty. She smiled referring to her one infirmity, and when she smiled the parchment of her face became like the surface of the most ancient palimpsest: it was seamed by a thousand of the finest lines, and made me feel that I was looking at an original etching by Rembrandt or Albert Dürer—a "trial proof," not evenly bitten in places; and the cap she wore added to the illusion.

She was, I could see, what might be called a professional centenarian, and so might retain some of those prejudices which existed long ago against "talking shop" and therefore I refrained from referring in any way to her age: I felt sure that when the right moment came she would give me an opening, and I found that I had not misjudged her. I had scarcely told her how greatly we all liked our house before she gratified me by a reminiscence of the antepenultimate owner: he had died, I happen to know, thirty-eight years ago, and Mrs. Trendall remembered the morning he first rode his black horse to hounds—that was the year before he married, and his son was now a major-general. "A long time ago," I remarked, and she smiled the patronising smile of the professional at the feeble effort of an incompetent amateur. "Long ago? Oh no; only a bit over sixty years—maybe seventy." The difference between sixty and seventy years ago was in her eyes not worth taking any account of. Her treatment of this reminiscence gave me warning of what she could do when she had her second wind and got into her stride.

"You must have a great memory, Mrs. Trendall," I remarked. "Was there much stir in this neighbourhood when Queen Victoria got married? I heard something about a big bonfire on Earl's Beacon."

"'Twere no more'n a lucifer match in compare with the flare up after Waterloo," was her complacent reply; and I felt as if I had just had an audacious pawn taken by my opponent's Queen. "Ay, Thurswell lost three fine youngsters at Waterloo. There was Amos Scovell, him with the red hair."

"The one they used to call Carrots?" I suggested.

She brightened up.

"The very same—Carrots they called him sure enough," she said, nodding. "But you couldn't have knowed'un; you're no more'n a stripling as yet. Doan't you list to all that you hear from them that calls theirselves ancient old venerables; there's not a one of'un that's truthfully old—I'm the only one; take my word for it, sir."

I gave her to understand (I hope) by my confidential smile and shake of the head that I was aware of the many fraudulent claims to longevity advanced by some of our friends about Thurswell.

"Age? Age is an empty thing without a memory," I remarked. "But what a memory you have, Mrs. Trendall! I shouldn't wonder if you recollected the news of Nelson's victory at Trafalgar arriving in England—oh no: that was too long ago even for you."

She bridled up in a moment.

9

"Too long ago for me?—too long, quotha! Don't I mind it as if it happened no earlier'n last week? It were before I married my first. It were my father that came a-bustling hasty like and wi' a face rosy wi' beer and hurry, and says he, 'Nelson has broke the Frenchies on us—broke them noble, and we may look for'un coming home any day now,' says he; and there wasn't a sober man in the five parishes that night—no, not a one. Ay, those was times!"

"Surely—surely," I acquiesced. "But now that you can look back on them quite calmly in the afternoon of your life, would you really say that they were more lively times than when the Duke of Marlborough was doing his fighting for us? You've heard your mother speak of Marlborough, I'm sure."

"My mother—speak! Why, I see'un for myself wi' these very eyes when he come home from the wars—a nice, well-set-up gentleman, if so be that I know what'tis to be a gentleman. It was when he come to pay his respex to Squire Longden at Old Deane—the squire that married thrice, as they said, the first for love, the second for lucre, and the third for—for—now was it for liquor or learning?—Well, 'twere one of the two. Ay, sir, those was the times —before there was any talk about Prince Albert and the Christian Palace in London."

"I should rather think so. And if you are old enough to remember seeing the great Duke of Marlborough, I am sure that you may remember seeing Oliver Cromwell when he came through Thurswell with his army?"

"Oliver Cromwell? You've spoke the truth, sir. I see'un once—on'y once, to be exact. I mind'un well.'Twere in the mid o' hay harvest, and father come up to us in a mortial great haste, and says he, 'Martha lass, throw down that rake and I'll show you the greatest sight o' your life—Cromwell hisself on a mighty skewbald.' And, sure enough, there he was a-galloping at the head of a fine army o' men, with guns a-rumbling and the bugles blowing—grand as a circus—ay, Batty's Circus with all the fun about Jump Jim Crow and Billy Barlow and the rest. Oh, I saw'un sure."

"And Queen Elizabeth—I wonder if you ever chanced to see her?"

"Never, sir—never! 'Twere always the sorrow o' my life that the day she passed through Ticebourne, where I was living with my grand-aunt Martha— her that I was named after—I had been sent with a basket o' three dozen eggs —one dozen of'em turkeys—to the big house, and her ladyship not being at home I had to wait the best part of a whole hour, and by the time I got back the Queen had driven away, so I missed the chance o' my life; for being since my early years noteworthy for speaking the truth to a hairs-breadth, I couldn't bring myself to say that I had seen a royal person when I hadn't. But what I can say is that I on'y missed seeing of her by twenty minutes, more or less."

I began to feel that I might be overwhelmed if I were borne much farther in the current of the pellucid stream of Mrs. Trendall's veracity; so I rose and thanked the good woman for her courtesy, and expressed the hope that the efforts she had made on my behalf to be rigidly accurate had not fatigued her.

She assured me that all she had said was nothing to what she could say if I had a mind to listen to her.

When I acknowledged to the Rector that the memory of Martha had surpassed my most sanguine hopes, he was greatly delighted. I thought it well, however, to neglect the opportunity he gave me of going into the details of her interesting recollections. Before we dropped the subject, he said what a pity it was that an historian of the nineteenth century could not avail himself of the services of Martha to keep him straight on some points that might be pronounced of a contentious nature.

Not many days after my interesting interview with Martha, the professional centenarian, the decease of an unobtrusive amateur was notified to me. It came about through the temporary disorganisation of our bread service, which I learned was due to the sudden death of the baker's mother. Entering his shop a week or two later, I ventured to say a word of conventional condolence to him, and this was responded to by him with a mournful volubility that made me feel as if I had just attended a funeral oration, or an inefficient reading of "In Memoriam." It was a terrible blow to him, he said—a cruel blow; and he went on to suggest that it was such an apparently gratuitous stroke that it made even the most orthodox man doubt the existence of mercy in the Hand that had inflicted it.

"No doubt, no doubt," I acquiesced. "But, after all, we must all die some day, Martin, and your good mother could scarcely be said to have been cut off long before she had reached the allotted span. You know you can hardly call yourself a young man still, Martin."

He shook his head as if to hint that he had heard this sort of thing before. I think it very probable that he had: I know that I had, more than once. But I thought that there was no occasion for him to suggest so much, so I boldly asked him what age his mother had reached.

He shook his head, not laterally this time, but longitudinally, and distributing the flies more evenly over a plate of jam tarts with a mournful whisk of his feather duster, he replied—

"She was a hundred and four last February, sir."

I turned right about and left him alone with his irreparable grief.

II. THE POINT OF VIEW

On the subject of age, I may say that it has always seemed to me that it is the aim of most people to appear as young as possible—and perhaps even more so—for as long as possible—and perhaps even longer; but then it seems gradually to dawn upon them that there may be as much distinction attached to age as to youth, and those who have been trying to pass themselves off as much younger than they really are turn their attention in the other direction and endeavour to make themselves out to be much older than the number of their years. It is, of course, chiefly in the cottages that the real veterans are to be found—old men and women who take a proper pride in having reached a great if somewhat indefinite age, and in holding in contempt the efforts of a neighbour to rival them in this way. One of the peculiarities of these good folk is to become hilarious over the news of the death of some contemporary. I have seen ancient men chuckle at the notion of their having survived some neighbour who, they averred with great emphasis, was much their junior. The idea seems to strike them as being highly humorous. And so perhaps it may be, humour being so highly dependent upon the standpoint from which it is viewed.

In the cottages the conversation frequently turns upon the probability of an aged inmate being gathered unto his fathers before next harvest or, if in autumn, before the first snow, and the utmost frankness characterises the remarks made on this subject in the presence of the person who might be supposed to be the most interested in the discussion, though, as a matter of fact, he is as little interested in it as the Tichborne claimant acknowledged he was in his trial after it had passed its fortieth day. I was fortunate enough to reach the shelter of a farm cottage before a great storm a few years ago, and on a truckle bed in the warm side of the living room of the family there lay an old man, who nodded to me and quavered out a "good marn." I asked the woman, who was peeling potatoes sitting on a stool, if he was her father or her husband's father.

"He's Grandpaw Beck; but don't you take any heed o' him, sir, he's dying," she replied, with the utmost cheerfulness. "Doctor's bin here yestereve, and says he'll be laid out afore a week. But we've everything handylike and ready for'un."

She pointed to a chair on which some white garments were neatly laid. "I run the iron o'er'em afore settin' to the bit o' dinner," she explained.

I glanced at the old man. He nodded his approval of her good housekeeping. He clearly thought that procrastination should be discountenanced.

The flashes of lightning and the peals of thunder seemed to me to be by no means extravagant accompaniments to this grim scene (as it appeared in my eyes). I have certainly known far less impressive scenes on the stage thought worthy of the illumination of lightning and the punctuation of thunder claps.

This familiar treatment of the subject of the coming of the grim figure with the scythe prevails in every direction. A friend of mine had a like experience in a cottage in another part of the country. The man of the house—he was a farm labourer—was about to emigrate to Canada, and was anxious to get as good a price as possible for some pieces of old china in his possession, and my friend had called to see them by invitation. He was brought into a bedroom where the plates were to be seen on a dresser; and by way of making conversation on entering the room, he asked the man when he thought of leaving England.

"Oh, very shortly now," he replied. "Just as soon as feyther there dies" (jerking his head in the direction of a bed), "and he's far gone—he's dying fast—Doctor Jaffray gives us great hope that a week'll finish'un."

He then went on to talk about the china, explaining that three of the pieces had been brought by his grandmother from the Manor House, where she had been still-room maid for twenty-six years.

"Twenty-eight years—twenty-eight years, Amos," came a correcting falsetto from the bed.

"You know nowt o' the matter," cried the son. "This is no business o' yours. We doan't want none o' your jaw. Go on wi' your dying."

CHAPTER TWO.—OUTSIDE THE VILLAGE

I.   —THE GENERAL

ON A VERY DIFFERENT PLANE OF INterest I regard my experience of two delightful old people whom I found living, the one a mile or two on the Brindlington side of Thurswell, the other on the Broadminster side, "where the Dean lives." The former is an old general who once commanded a regiment of Sikhs and spent fifty years in India. He is now eighty-three years of age, and has two sons with the rank of colonel, a grandson who is a captain of Sappers, and two who are lieutenants in the navy. The old man has nothing of the bristling retired general about him—not even the liver. He is of a gentle, genial nature, not very anxious to hear the latest news, and not at all eager to make his visitors acquainted with his experiences in India or his views as to the exact degree of decadence reached by "the sarvice." He speaks in a low and an almost apologetic tone, and is interested in old Oriental china and tortoiseshell tea-caddies. One could never believe that this was the man whose sobriquet of Shire-i-Iran (Lion of Persia) was once a household word along the turbulent northwest frontier, or that he had been the most brilliant exponent of all the dash which one associates with the cavalry leader. His reputation on that long frontier was that of an Oriental equivalent of the Wild Huntsman of the German ballad. People had visions of him galloping by night at the head of his splendid Sikhs to cut off the latest fanatical insurrectionary from his supports, and then sweep him and his marauders off the face of the earth. Certainly no cavalry leader ever handled his men with that daring which he displayed—a daring that would have deserved to be called recklessness had it once failed…. And there he sat at dinner, talking in his low voice about the fluted rim of one of his tea-caddies, and explaining how it was quite possible to repair the silver stringing that beautified the top. Once I fancied I overheard him telling the person who sat by him at dinner about the native regiments—I felt sure that I heard the word "Sepoy," and I became alert. Alas! the word that I had caught was only "tea-poy"—he was telling how he had got a finely cut glass for a deficient caddie out of an old nineteenth-century mahogany tea-poy. That was the nearest approach he made to the days of his greatness.

But I noticed with satisfaction that he partook of every dish that was offered to him—down to the marmalade pudding. At dessert he glanced down the table and said that he thought he would have an apple. "No, dear," said his daughter, gently but firmly removing the dish beyond his reach. "You know that you are not allowed to touch apples."

"Why, what harm will an apple do me—just one—only one apple?" he inquired, and there were tears in his voice—it had become a tremulous pipe, the tone of a child whose treat had been unjustly curtailed. "No, dear, not even one. It is for your own good: you should have an apple if it agreed with you; but it doesn't."

"I want an apple—I can't see what harm an apple would do me," he cried again. But his daughter was firm. It was very pathetic to witness the scene. The Lion of Persia becoming plaintive at being denied a rosy-cheeked apple. The man who, with a force of only six hundred sabres behind him, had ridden up to Mir Ali Singh with the three thousand rebels supporting him, and demanded his sword, and got it, not being able to get his apple when he had asked for it nicely, seemed to me to be a most pathetic figure. I pleaded for him as one pleads for a child in the nursery: he had been a good boy and had eaten all that had been set before him quite nicely—why might he not have an apple to make him happy?

But the daughter was inexorable. She told me that I did not know her father, while she did. An apple would be poison to him; and so the old hero was left complaining, with an occasional falsetto note, upon the restrictions of his commissariat. I am pretty sure that there was no falsetto note in any of his complaints in regard to commissariat forty years ago.

He was a noble old warrior, however, for when his daughter had, with the rest of the ladies, left us after dinner, he never put out a hand to the apple dish, though there was no man at the table who would have interfered with him had he done so; the Newtown Pippins remained blushing, but not on account of any disloyalty on his part to the duty he owed to the daughter who had his welfare at heart.

II.   —THE DEAR OLD LADY

The aged lady who lives in a lovely old moated house a few miles out of Thurswell is one of the youngest people I ever met. She is the mother of two distinguished sons and the grandmother of a peeress. She takes an interest in everything that is going on in various parts of the world, and even points out the mistakes made by the leader-writers in the London papers—some of the mistakes. But she does so quite cheerfully and without any animus. She still sketches *en plein air*, and in her drawings there is no suggestion of the drawing-master of the early Victorians. Any elderly person who could hold a pencil and whose moral character could bear a strict investigation was accounted competent to teach drawing in those days; for drawing in those days meant nothing beyond making a fair copy of a lithograph of a cottage in a wood with a ladder leaning against a gable and a child sitting on a fence—a possible successful statesman in the future—with a dog below him. She never was so taught, she told me: she had always held out against the restrictions of the schoolroom of her young days, and had never played either the "Maiden's Prayer" or the "Battle of Prague." Thalberg's variations on "Home Sweet Home" she had been compelled to learn. No young lady in that era of young ladies could avoid acquiring at least the skeleton of Thalberg's masterpiece: and I was glad that this particular old lady, who had once been a young lady, had mastered it; for it enabled her to give me the most delightful parody upon it that could be imagined.

Only once did I hear her speak with bitterness in referring to any one; but when she began upon this occasion, she spoke not only bitterly, but wrathfully—contemptuously as well. She was referring to the Emperor Napoleon III. in his relations with the unhappy Maximilian of Mexico. She had known the latter intimately. My own impression is that she had been in love with him—and tears were in her eyes when she talked of how he had been betrayed by the man whom she called a contemptible little cad. Sedan represented, in her way of thinking, the cordial agreement with her views by the Powers above. To hear her talk of those tragedies of more than forty years ago, as if they were the incidents of the day before yesterday, was inspiriting. I never inquired what was her age, but one afternoon when I called upon her I found that a birthday party was going on—a double party; for it was her birthday as well as her youngest grandchild's. Two fully iced cakes, with pink and white complexions, were being illuminated in the customary way, and each had been made a candelabrum of eight tapers. When I ventured to suggest that there must be an error in computation in some direction, it was the younger of the beneficiaries who explained to me that about seventy years or so ago Granny had become too old to allow of her birthday cake holding the full amount of the candles to which she was entitled, so it had been agreed that she should have only one candle for every ten years of her life. The little girl confided in me that she thought it was rather a shame to cheat poor Granny out of her rights, but of course there was no help for it: any one could see that no cake could be made large enough to accommodate, without undue crowding, eighty-one candles.

I looked at the sweet old Granny, and thought, for some reason or other, of the night of the first January of the century when I had stood listening to the tolling of the eighty-one strokes of the church bell in Devonshire, when every belfry in the kingdom announced the age of the good Queen who had gone to her rest. I wondered...

This dear lady of the eight-candle birthday cake—of which, by the bye, she partook heartily and apparently without the least misgiving—had been married at the age of seventeen, and this, she thought, was exactly the right age for a girl to marry, not, as might be supposed, because it admitted of her period of repentance being so much the longer, but simply because she considered grandchildren so interesting. She was not inclined to be tolerant over the prudent marriages of the present day, when no girl is unreasonable enough to expect a proposal before she is twenty-five, or from a man who is less than thirty-five. It almost brought me back to Shakespeare's England to hear her express such opinions. That stately old lady, Juliet's mother, as she appears in every modern production of the play, was made by the author to be something between twenty-six and twenty-seven, her daughter being some months under fourteen, but certainly forward for her age. We used to be informed by sage critics of this drama "of utter love defeated utterly" that Shakespeare made Juliet so young because it was the custom in Italy, where girls developed into womanhood at a much earlier age than in England, for a girl to marry at Juliet's time of life. It so happens, however, that early marriage was the custom in England and not in Italy in the sixteenth century. When a girl was twelve her parents looked about for a promising husband for her, and usually found one when she was thirteen.

Only a few months ago I came upon an unpublished letter, written in the beautiful Gothic hand of Queen Elizabeth, in response to the inquiry of an ambassador respecting a wife for an amiable young prince. The Queen suggested two names of highly eligible young women, and mentioned that one of them was twelve and the other thirteen!

The most flagrant example of unbridled centenarianism which I have yet come across in the course of my investigations in the neighbourhood of

Thurswell was that of a lady who had won quite a literary aureole for her silver hair owing to the accident of her being actually the original "Cousin Amy" of Tennyson's "Locksley Hall." For years she had worn this honourable distinction, and, so far as I could gather, her title to it had never been disputed. Even in the Cathedral Close of Broadminster the tradition had been accepted, and she had been pointed out to strangers, who doubtless looked at her with interest, saying, "Not really!" or "How perfectly sweet!"

I ventured to ask the prebendary who had told me that the poet had been in love with her and consequently "greatly cut up" when she married some one else—as might be inferred from some passages in the poem—what was the present age of the lady, and he assured me that she was seventy-four. She did not look it, but she really was seventy-four. I had not the heart to point out that twenty-three years had elapsed since Tennyson published his sequel —"Sixty Years After"—to his "Locksley Hall," so that this "Cousin Amy" must be at least a centenarian if she had not died, as described in the sequel, between eighty and ninety years ago. She was, however, a nice old lady and her name was really Amy, and she had known Alfred Tennyson when she had been very young and he a middle-aged gentleman whom it was a great privilege to know.

CHAPTER THREE—THE VILLAGE VILLAS

I.   —THE PILLARS OF SOCIETY

THURSWELL IS UNDOUBTEDLY AN IDeal English village situated in the midst of an agricultural county, and far away from the unhealthy and demoralising influences of trade. It prides itself on being "select"—so does every other English village, even when it lies deep embowered among the striking scenery of a coal-mining district. But Thurswell is really "select." A strange family may come to one of the best houses—one of the four or five that have entrance gates with lodges and carriage drives—and yet remain absolutely ignored by the older residents. Of course the shopkeepers pay the newcomers some little attention, and the ladies who collect for the various charities and the various churches are quite polite in making early calls; but the question of calling formally and leaving cards simply because the people are newcomers, requires to be thoroughly threshed out before it is followed by any active movement on the part of the senior residents. It has been called unsocial on this account; but everybody in the world—at least, everybody in Thurswell—knows that to be called unsocial is only another way of being called select The Rector must pronounce an opinion on the strangers, and—more important still—the Rector's wife. The example of the Barnaby-Granges, who have lived for centuries at the Moated Manor House, must be observed for what it is worth. It is understood that people like the Barnaby-Granges may call upon strangers out of a sense of duty; but every one knows how far astray from the path trod by the "select" a sense of duty may lead one, so that the fact of the Manor House people having called upon the newcomer is not invariably regarded as conferring upon the latter the privilege of a passport to the most representative Society at Thurswell. The strangers must wait until Mrs. Lingard and Miss Mercer have decided whether they are to be called on or ignored. Mrs. Lingard is the widow of a captain of Sappers, and Miss Mercer is the middle-aged daughter of a previous rector, and for years these ladies have assumed the right of veto in respect of the question of calling upon newcomers. Within the past year, however, this question, it should be mentioned, has developed certain complications, owing to the strained relations existing between the two ladies. Previously they formed a sort of vigilance committee to determine what should be done, but since the breaking off of diplomatic relations between them the poor people who had previously looked to them jointly for guidance are now compelled to consult them severally as to the course they mean to pursue, and all this takes time, and the loss of time in the etiquette of first calls may be construed into actual rudeness by sensitive people.

That is how we stand at present; and although many well-meaning persons —not invariably belonging to clerical circles—have endeavoured to bring about a *rapprochement* for the good of the whole community between Mrs. Lingard and Miss Mercer, hitherto every effort of the kind has failed.

When the particulars of the incident that brought about the friction between the two ladies are known, it will easily be understood that a restoration of the *status quo ante* is not to be accomplished in a moment.

It was all due to the exceptionally dry summer. People who retain only the pleasantest recollections of that season of sunlight and balmy breezes will probably find reason to modify their views respecting it when they hear how it led to the shattering of an old friendship and, incidentally, to the complication of the most important social question that can come before such a community as is represented by Thurs-well.

II.—THE SHATTERING OF THE PILLARS

The facts of the matter are simple enough in their way. Each of the ladies occupies a small house of her own, fully, and not semi-detached, with a small patch of green in front and a small garden at the back; but the combined needs of front and back are not considered sufficiently great to take up all the time of a gardener working six days in the week during the summer. There is enough work, however, to take up three days of the six, with window-cleaning thrown in, in slack seasons. As the conditions of labour are identical in the case of the gardens of both ladies—only Miss Mercer throws in the washing of her pug to balance Mrs. Lingard's window-cleaning—John Bingham, the jobbing gardener of Thurswell, suggested several years ago that he should divide his time between the two gardens, and this plan, to all appearances, worked very satisfactorily in regard to every one concerned.

THE JOBBING GARDENER

24

Only John Bingham was aware of the trouble involved in keeping both gardens on precisely the same level of "getting on"—only John Bingham was aware of the difficulty of preventing either of the ladies from seeing that anything in the garden of the other was "getting on" better than the same thing in her own patch. It might have been fancied that as they were in complete agreement respecting the necessity for a strict censorship upon the visiting lists of the neighbourhood as regards strangers, there could not possibly exist any rivalry between them on so insignificant a matter as the growth of a petunia or the campanile of a campanula; but John Bingham knew better. It had been his task year by year to minimise to the one lady his success with the garden of the other—to say a word of disparagement on Thursdays, Fridays, and Saturdays of all that he had been praising on Mondays, Tuesdays, and Wednesdays. But sometimes Nature is stronger even than her greatest enemy, a jobbing gardener, and so it was that when Mrs. Lingard chanced to pay a visit to Miss Mercer on a Thursday, she found the garden of the latter, just recovering from the hand of John Bingham's attention on the Monday, Tuesday, and Wednesday, obviously superior in some respects to her own, and John found his diplomatic resources quite unable to meet with the demand for an explanation when she got home. It was in vain that he tried to make her understand, what she certainly should have known already from her experience of the ministrations of John—namely, that not he, but the superior soil and aspect of Miss Mercer's herbaceous border, should be regarded accountable for the marvellous growths which had attracted her attention in the garden of her rival. His Thursday, Friday, and Saturday patron declared herself far from satisfied with such an explanation. Soil! Had she ever shown herself to be close-fisted in the matter of soil? she inquired. And as for aspect—had he not chosen the aspect of the herbaceous border at which he was now working? No, she knew very well, she affirmed, that what made a garden beautiful was loving care. She professed herself unable to understand why John should lavish all his affection upon Miss Mercer's border rather than upon her own; all that she could do was to judge by results, and, viewed from this basis, it could not but be apparent to every unprejudiced observer that he had been giving Miss Mercer's borders such loving touches as he had never bestowed upon her own: the flowers spoke for themselves.

John had heard of the Language of Flowers, but he had never mastered the elements of their speech. As a matter of fact, he took no interest in flowers or their habits. He had "dratted" them times without number for their failure to do all that the illustrated catalogues declared they would do, and now he found reason to drat those of Miss Mercer for having done much more than he had meant them to do. It was with a view to restore the balance of mediocrity between the gardens, which had been through no fault of his, disturbed by a sudden outbreak of "Blushing Brides" in Miss Mercer's parterre, that he gave some extra waterings to Mrs. Lingard's verbinas, trusting to convince her that he was a thoroughly disinterested operator in both the gardens—which was certainly a fact. But in that arid summer the response of the verbinas was but too rapid, and Miss Mercer, calling upon her friend (and rival), was shown the bed with the same pride that she had displayed when exhibiting her petunias.

She said nothing—the day was Saturday—but she perceived, with that unerring intuition which in some persons almost takes the place of genius, that petunias had been supplanted (literally) by verbinas in the affections of John Bingham.

She spent the Sunday rehearsing an interview which she had arranged in her mind to have with John Bingham when he should arrive the next day.

But Monday came, and John Bingham failed to arrive. She waited at the back entrance to the garden until ten o'clock, but still he did not appear. Then she sent a messenger to his cottage to inquire the cause of his absence. Monday, Tuesday, and Wednesday were her days for his services, and never once had he failed her. She could not guess what was the matter. She had always regarded him as a sober man and one for whom Monday morning had no terrors. The mystery of his first failure was rendered all the more unfathomable when the tweeny maid returned saying that Mrs. Bingham had told her positive that John had gone out to work as usual that same morning, and that Mrs. Bingham had taken it for granted that he was in Miss Mercer's garden.

For a quarter of an hour Miss Mercer pondered over the whole incident, and then she suddenly put on another hat, discarding the garden specimen with which she had begun the day, and went down the road and round by the Moated Manor House to where Mrs. Lingard's villa was situated, just beyond the knoll of elms. The hall door was wide open to the morning air, and through the glass door at the farther end of the hall she distinctly saw Mrs. Lingard standing on the edge of one of the beds of the garden with John Bingham kneeling at her feet.

And this on a Monday morning!

John Bingham had actually attended morning ser-vice in the church the day before—Miss Mercer had seen him there—and yet on Monday he had broken faith with her, and now, at ten-thirty, he was engaged in planting out the contents of the capacious basket which Mrs. Lingard was doling out to him.

And Mrs. Lingard was wearing her garden hat just as if the day was

Thursday, Friday, or Saturday, when she was entitled to his services.

And Mrs. Lingard had also been at church the previous day and had repeated the responses in her ordinary tone of voice, and without faltering, though beyond a doubt her heart had been full of this scheme of suborning a faithful, if somewhat weak, servant from his allegiance to the mistress who had an undisputed claim to his services the next day!

Without a moment's hesitation Miss Mercer passed into the hall, opened the glass door beyond, and stood beside the guilty pair before either of them was aware of her presence. She saw that the man was planting asters—the finest aster cuttings she had ever seen.

"John Bingham, are you aware that this is Monday morning?" she said in an accusing voice, and so suddenly that a cry of surprise—it may have been with guilt—came from Mrs. Lingard, and John Bingham let drop his trowel and wiped his forehead.

"Good gracious, Lucy! Where did you drop from without warning?" cried the lady in the garden hat.

"I am addressing John Bingham, madam," said Miss Mercer in icy tones. "And once again I ask John Bingham what he means by being here when his place should be in my garden."

"I can easily explain, my good woman," said Mrs. Lingard, lapsing, under the "madam" of the other, into the tone of voice she had found effective with the native servants in the West Indian island of St. Lucia when her husband had been stationed there.

"I am not addressing you, madam," said Miss Mercer hotly: her glacial period had passed and had given place to the volcanic—the suppressed volcanic. "I wish to be informed why this man—this traitor—this—this——"

"Don't be a greater fool than you are by nature, my good creature," said Mrs. Lingard. "But I might have known that you could be disagreeable over even such a trifle as my sending to John Bingham to assist me for an hour in planting out the asters which were only delivered this morning when they should have been here on Saturday. If I had not begged him to come to my help for a couple of hours the lot would have been spoiled. In justice to him I will say that he was very unwilling to come."

"And what does that mean, pray?" asked Miss Mercer sneeringly.

"It means that he knew you better than I did," responded Mrs. Lingard. "He has had more experience of your narrow-mindedness than I have had. Now, go on with your work, John. Don't mind her."

But John did not go on with his work. He touched his forehead with the drooping aster that he held rather limply, saying, in the direction of Miss Mercer—"I can easy make up the extra however, ma'am—mortal easy, in the evenin', and so I thought or I wouldn't be here now."

"There, let that satisfy you, make your mind easy; you'll not be defrauded of the shilling for his two hours," said Mrs. Lingard.

"You will be good enough to dictate to your inferiors, if such exist, madam; you need not dictate to me. You may keep your John Bingham now that you have him; I have made other arrangements for the future of my garden."

She turned with a mock courtesy. Mrs. Lingard also turned.

"Lucy Mercer, go back to your—your—your hen-run," she cried, pointing dramatically to the place of exit. "Go on with your work, John Bingham. Mrs. Hopewell will only be too glad to take on your Thursdays, Fridays, and Saturdays. *She* has a garden—*a garden.*"

That is the true and circumstantial account of how Mrs. Lingard and Miss Mercer ceased to be on speaking terms, and that is how it is that many people are becoming more hopeful of the future of Thurswell as the centre of a social neighbourhood. Each lady still arrogates to herself the right of veto in respect of the claims of any strange family to be visited on taking up their residence within reasonable visiting distance of Thurswell; but the people who formerly had been ready to accept the dictum of the two in such social matters are now beginning not only to assert their own independence of action, but even to dictate to others on all points on which they themselves had been dictated to —in no mild way—by Mrs. Lingard and Miss Mercer. But a mistake that was recently made by one of these immature dictators has done much to chasten their longing to take up the responsibilities attached to such a position. She had spoken with that definiteness which marks the amateur on the subject of the visiting of a certain Mrs. Judson Hyphen Marks who had taken Higham Lodge for a year, and accordingly quite a number of people left cards upon her. But suddenly the name of Judson Hyphen Marks appeared rather prominently in the columns devoted to the Law Court proceedings in the daily papers, and some curious information respecting the *ménage* of the Judson Hyphen Marks was brought under the notice of the people of Thurswell and, indeed, of England generally; and those who had left cards upon them consulted together as to whether it was possible or not for them to ask for their cards to be returned to them.

The general opinion that prevailed after several long discussions on this question was that no social machinery existed by which so desirable an object might be effected, and no move was made in that direction; but ever afterward the dictation of the feeble amateur who thought to take the social reins out of the hands of Mrs. Lingard and Miss Mercer when it was found that they were pulling them in opposite directions, threatening to upset the social apple-cart, was received for what it was worth, not for what it claimed to be worth.

III.   —FLOWERS AND FRIENDSHIPS

The instance just recorded of horticulture playing a prominent part in the breaking up of friendships is by no means unique. When one comes to think of it, one cannot be surprised that as the earliest serious quarrel recorded in the history of the world was over a purely horticultural question—namely, whether or not the qualities of beneficent nutrition attributed to a certain fruit had been accurately analysed—there should be many differences of opinion among the best of friends on the same subject.

It was my old gardener—not-the oldest of all, but the second oldest—who told me how it was that the annual prize given by the Moated Manor House people for the best floral display of the cottage order was very nearly withdrawn for ever, owing to the bad blood that was made by the award, no matter in what direction it was made. It seemed that the prize-winner invariably found himself compelled to accept the challenge to fight of all the disappointed aspirants to the prize, and before nightfall there was a general distribution of black eyes and front teeth; in some cases both got inextricably mixed up, and this was no pleasure to anybody, my informant assured me, and the wives of the men who were keen to compete for the prize discouraged them from it, with the warning that if they continued to spend their time over the cultivation of the blooms they might some day actually find themselves awarded the prize. That warning, founded as it was upon sound sense and reason, was beginning to produce its effects upon the better class of flower growers; but there were still a number of young fellows who went into training at the punch ball at the Church Institute club-room the day they sowed their flower seeds, and so were at the top of their form when the award was made in the early autumn, so that if one of them got the prize he thought if a pity that his training and practice at the punch ball should be wasted, and thus he was ready to prove to all disputants that the prize had gone to the best man; while it was only to be expected that those who had only had the cold consolation of honorary mention were only too ready to dispute his ability to maintain such an attitude for any length of time.

The result of this joint cultivation of bulbs and biceps was not just what the givers of the prize intended to achieve, and twice, when there had been arrests and summonses to petty sessions, a formal warning was issued to all whom it might concern that if the connection between the two cultures were not severed, the prize, which was only meant for success in the one, would be withdrawn.

Happily, however, it was not found necessary to enforce this ultimatum, and a *modus vivendi,* founded upon one which had been understood to work very satisfactorily in the case of the Chrysanthemum Society of Mallingham, was adopted, and up to the present this had made for peace. The annual Battle of Flowers at Thurswell has become a thing of the past, and "Midge" Purcell, the ex-lightweight champion of the county, who rents the Lion and Lamb Inn, and to whom the candidates for the prize applied for advice on the biceps side of the joint contest, affirms with regret that Englishmen are becoming degenerate.

It was a peace-loving florist at Mallingham, the honorary secretary to the Chrysanthemum Society, who explained the system upon which his committee had agreed to make their awards, and urged its adoption by the Thurswell people. Its operation was not intricate. Its fundamental principle may best be defined on the analogy of the rotation of crops as the rotation of awards. Like the award of the Garter, merit had nothing to do with its scheme. The prizes were awarded strictly in turn to the professional competitors—the others did not matter. Mr. Johnson got the chrysanthemum cup one year, Mr. Thompson the medal for the best twelve cut lilies, Mr. Cardwell the Malmaison salver, and Mr. Prior the vase for the best display of greenhouse ferns. The next year it was arranged that the vase should go to Mr. Johnson, the salver to Mr. Thompson, and so forth. By the adoption of this admirable plan the judges were saved a large amount of trouble, and there never was any friction between the competitors, for it was understood that if it was Prior's year for the lily medal, but he had a liking for any other prize, he could nearly always negotiate an exchange with the man whose turn had come for the award that he fancied. This principle of give and take, live and let live, had made the Mallingham Society one of the most popular floricultural organisations in the country, and its adoption by the Thurswell Committee of the Manor House prize brought about, as has been said, an entire cessation of that ill-feeling which led to the use of language that was certainly not the language of flowers, and to many-discreditable scenes even when there were no arrests made. The cause of peace has triumphed, though some people say that floriculture languishes through the lack of heal thy rivalry; for when every man is certain of the prize when his turn comes for it, he does not trouble about the flowers. There may be something in this suggestion.

Taking one consideration with another, it really does seem a pity that the rotation system is not more widely accepted by those societies which have been established for the encouragement of sundry excellent objects, such as the breeding of bull-dogs (for symbolic purposes), of pugs (of no use to any one when they are bred), of pigs (of which the prize-winner is invariably the most uneatable), and of pets (in various forms). In our neighbourhood such organisations are to be numbered by the dozen, and after every prize distribution the air is murmurous with the complaints of disappointed competitors. It was a shrewd farmer who suggested to me the principle on which the awards are made at our local dog show. "The reason why there's so much grumbling, sir, is because the judges look at the wrong end of the leash," he said, and I understood what he meant.

"JUDGES LOOK AT THE WRONG END OF THE LEASH"

I know that the impression is very general that the pedigree of the exhibitor rather than that of the exhibit influences the local judges.

But I must confess that I could not bring myself to sympathise with one of our new residents who, after living in London all his life, bought Harley Croft House, a 40 h.p. motor-car and six pairs of gaiters, and set up as a country gentleman. It must be acknowledged that at times he looked a colourable imitation of one. He hoped that his starting of the breeding of cattle and fowl would consolidate his position. But his researches in the literature of both subjects at the same time resulted in some confusion. Of course his pointing out some drab-tinted cows to the steward of the Manor and alluding to them definitely as Buff Orpingtons was a slip that any one might make; but to hope to win sympathy for a wrong done to him by the judges at the poultry show by affirming that his bantam cock was really twice the size of the one to which the prize had been awarded was, I think, a strategical mistake of a flagrant character.

Much more in the spirit of the country gentleman was the remark made to me by a neighbour who hunts five days a week in winter and talks about hunting seven days a week in the summer, on a purely literary subject. He had been at the Military Tournament in London the year that *The Merchant of Venice* was being played at Her Majesty's Theatre, and he confided in me that he thought on the whole it was very fine indeed, though for his part he enjoyed *The Runaway Girl* at the Gaiety more fully. He could not quite understand the point of some of the jokes in *The Merchant of Venice*, he said. For instance, he should like to know what there was to laugh at in the chap's saying to the Jew that some one had shown him a turquoise which he had bought from the Jew's daughter for a monkey. Any one who knew anything about precious stones knew that to pay a monkey for a single turquoise, even though set in an 18-carat ring, was to pay a fair price. Of course you couldn't get much of a diamond ring for twenty-five pounds; but you could get a first-rate turquoise for half the money. But there were some people, he knew, who would laugh at any joke if they were only told it was in a play of Shakespeare's. I agreed with him, and laughed.

That was not the sort of man who would make a fool of himself over Buff Orpingtons or cherish his bantams in proportion to their size and weight.

CHAPTER FOUR—THE COMEDIES OF THE COUNTRY HOUSE

I.   —LESSEES FROM THE MIDLANDS

It WAS THE REPRESENTATIVE OF THE second generation of one of the shirt-sleeves families of the midlands who took a lease of Nethershire Castle, the finest mansion in our neighbourhood. The Court of Chancery had decreed that it might be let for a term of years, the length of which was fixed by certain Commissioners in Lunacy, for Sir Ralph Richards had been in the care of a specialist in mental diseases for a long time, and it was understood that there were little hopes of his ever being able to enjoy his own again. Higgins was the name of the lessee from the north, and with his wife and family he had occupied the Castle for close upon ten years. He was a simple enough man as regards his tastes: he could not appreciate the beauty of the cedar wood ceiling of the banqueting hall or the Renaissance carved panels of the library. The splendid Gainsboroughs and Romneys of the Long Gallery made no more appeal to him than did the Van Dycks in the great hall or the three Fragonards of the drawing-room. He was quite satisfied with the reputation of having sufficient money to pay for the privilege of living in the midst of these masterpieces and of keeping about an acre and a half of roof in good repair: he knew more about the advantages of close-fitting slates than of the methods of eighteenth-century English artists or of fifteenth-century Italian carvers.

His wife, however, valued to the full the artistic privileges of living in so splendid a house, and she was not one to shrink before the searching glances of Frances Anne, the wife of the first baronet of the house of Richards, as painted by Sir Joshua, sacrificing to Venus, or to assume that Lady Elizabeth had turned aside from making a libation to Hymen—Hymen demanded quite as many sacrifices as Venus on eighteenth-century canvases—to ask her what right she had to sit in the seats of the Richards of Nethershire Castle. She knew what her husband paid in the way of rent, and she felt that the same was large enough to avert from her any indignant look that a sentimentalist might imagine on the face of the most malevolent family portrait. In fact, Mrs. Higgins considered the sum large enough to allow of her assuming the attitude of the patroness in regard to the pictures: she had actually been heard by a friend of the Richards to express a critical opinion respecting the pose of the daughter of the second baronet—the one who became well known as the Countess of Avonwater—in Romney's picture of her as Circe, and to suggest that the charger of Lieut.-Colonel Jack Churchill Richards—he was called after his father's great commander—in the picture by Sir Godfrey Kneller was scarcely large enough to make a polo pony. It was, however, clearly understood that these criticisms were offered by the lady only by way of establishing her rights over the contents of the mansion so long as her husband paid so handsomely as he did for the privilege of such an entourage. She had probably heard of certain rights-of-way being maintained by a formal walking over the ground to which they referred, by the claimant, once a year, and so she thought it well to walk over the pictures, so to speak, now and again to show that she understood the rights of her position. She really felt the greatest pride in everything, and in the course of a few years her feeling in regard to them was that of a conscientious descendant from illustrious ancestors. She was much prouder of them than the modern Major-General in *Patience* was of his ancestors acquired by purchase.

A visit that I paid to the Castle in the temporary possession of the family of Higgins was illuminating. I went not because I had ever met either Mr. or Mrs. Higgins, but because I was acquainted with Miss Richards, a charming old lady who was the sister of the unhappy baronet, and had been born in the Castle and lived there for twenty-five or thirty years, only leaving for the dower-house on the death of her mother.

Miss Richards was on the friendliest terms with the tenants of her old home, and I could see that they were pleased to welcome all the friends whom she might bring with her to see the wonders of the Castle. But it was Mrs. Higgins who "did the honours" of the picture gallery, when we went thitherward after tea one lovely afternoon in sum mer shortly after I had come to Thurswell. It was Mrs. Higgins who assumed the rôle of Cicerone and told me all about the pictures, and gave me duodecimo biographies of the originals with all the familiarity that one would expect only from a member of the family. Miss Richards stood by smiling quite pleasantly, even when Mrs. Higgins looked at her, saying something about a pink-coated Captain Richards by Raeburn, and I was disposed to laugh at the comedy of Mrs. Higgins of Lancashire telling Miss Richards of Nethershire something confidential about Captain Richards, her great-granduncle!

I admired the picture, but not nearly so much as I did the coolness of Mrs. Higgins and the kindly toleration of Miss Richards.

"And this is the portrait by Thornhill of Miss Esther Richards, who afterwards married General Forster, who took part in the American War, and to avenge the murder of poor André—he called it murder, though, of course, some people think that André was really a spy," said Mrs. Higgins. "Doesn't it seem strange to think of that sweet little girl-"

"Oh, pardon me," cried Miss Richards, "you are not quite right. That is Lotitia Richards by North-cote. She married Sir Charles Brewster, who was killed at Waterloo."

"Oh no," said the tenant, "you are quite wrong. I assure you that this is Esther. Your Lotitia is the girl in Oriental costume in the library."

"My dear Mrs. Higgins, how could I possibly be mistaken over such a matter?" said Miss Richards. "My dear mother told me how Letty Brewster came here one day when she was eighty-two years of age, and how pathetic it was to see her stand before her own picture done when a girl; but my mother said that really some of the charm of the picture—she had lovely eyes, as you can see—was apparent on the face of the dear old lady of eighty-two."

"I am afraid that you are mixing this picture with another," said Mrs. Higgins quite good-naturedly.

And then Miss Richards gave a laugh.

"We had better pass this picture and look at one which could not possibly be mixed up with another," she said. "I hope you will agree with me in believing that this is Hoppner's Lady Charlotte Richards, Mrs. Higgins."

"Oh yes, you are quite right about *that one*," said Mrs. Higgins as graciously as a governess commending the right answer given by an errant pupil. "Oh yes, that is Lady Charlotte. I believe she became pious and wrote a hymn. You have heard that, I suppose, Miss Richards?"

"I do believe I did," replied Miss Richards. "In fact, I have the tiny volume of hymns which she wrote. She was under the influence of Lady Huntingdon."

But Mrs. Higgins clearly took very little interest in Lady Huntingdon, and she went down the gallery making mistake after mistake; but Miss Richards never attempted to correct her—only once she caught my eye. Mrs. Higgins had attributed the Master Richards of Lawrence to Sir Peter Lely!

We were far away from the Castle before we had our laugh.

"Wasn't it really funny?" said Miss Richards.

"I think that you must be the most even-tempered person in the county, if not in all England," said I.

The friendly relations existing between the two ladies were not at all changed by the persistent patronage of the picture gallery by the one who was the tenant, and Mrs. Higgins was always ready to offer a hearty welcome to any of Miss Richards' friends and to do the honours of the Castle. I did not, however, trespass upon her hospitality a second time.

A year or two later I met a curious sort of gentleman who bore the same name as that of a family of considerable importance—county importance, I should say, for outside a ten-mile radius they are, as is usually the case, absolute nonentities. I had heard some say, however, that the family grounds included a rather wonderful fountain which I thought I should like to see. I asked the man if he was any relation to the family, and he replied, brightening up wonderfully, that they were his cousins.

"I believe they have a nice place," said I. "Isn't there a fountain that came from the Villa Borghese? I am greatly interested in that sort of thing."

"You must mean the one with the mermaids," said he.

"I dare say that is the one," said I.

"If you go in for things like that you should certainly see it," he cried. "Let me see how I can manage it."

"You are very kind," said I. "But I could not think of bothering you in the matter. I dare say that some day I shall have a chance———"

"I have it," he cried. "The family are going away for a fortnight at Easter, and when they are gone I could easily show you over the grounds. I'll just make sure of the day they leave, so that there may be no mistake."

In spite of a promise of such lavish hospitality, I resisted the temptation of being shown over the grounds in the way that was proposed: the fact being that I had no confidence in my own ability to act the part of the housekeeper's nephew or the second footman's uncle who are admitted to the great house when the family are away.

I trust, however, that I convinced the enterprising cousin of the great house that I fully appreciated his spirited offer to allow me a peep at the Borghese fountain through a chink in the back door, as it were.

I learned subsequently that the great family started in a tannery in Mallingham a hundred and twenty years ago. It was no wonder that any one in my station of life could only be expected to approach their demesne by a back way.

II.—THE LEGENDS OF THE COUNTRY HOUSE

On the subject of great houses, I may venture to say, it has always seemed to me to show a singular lack of imagination on the part of some one that one legend should be forced to do duty for so large a group, and this legend so devoid of any stimulating quality. It seems to me that the legends of the country houses of England are, like all Gaul, divided into three parts. All through the south one is shown the room in the mansion in which Queen Elizabeth slept. There is scarcely a Tudor house in which that particular monarch did not sleep for at least one night of her life, and so highly cherished is this family tradition that I have known of cases in which she slept in a room at least sixty years before the mansion itself was built. Then around London one is constantly pointed out by local antiquaries the house in which Nell Gwyn lived. "Madam Ellen" certainly seemed given to "flitting." A dozen houses at least are associated with her name. North of the Tweed we are confronted with the Mary Queen of Scots and the Bonnie Prince Charlie legends. Any story that fails to touch upon the vague history of the worthies whom I have ventured to name as presiding over each department of tradition, seems to be regarded as uninteresting. Although monarchs of quite as blessed memory as Queen Elizabeth must have slept in many mansions in their time, yet few rooms are consecrated to the memory of their slumbers, and although many ladies of the Court were quite as deserving of having their memory enshrined or ensign-ed in the name of a fully licensed public-house as Evelyn's "Impudent Comedian," yet none seem to be regarded as so good a draw as Nell Gwyn. The chairs of Mary Queen of Scots are as plentiful as the mementoes of the other Stuart worthies. I myself have seen in a mansion an Italian cabinet which I was assured had belonged to Queen Mary. But when I asked for evidence on this point I found that there was none forthcoming. I did not get so far as to make such an inquiry in the case of a mahogany looking-glass offered to me by a foolish dealer south of the Tweed, who declared that it had been in the possession of the same unfortunate lady. It was not to me, however, that another dealer tried to sell a dagger that had once been worn by the Young Pretender, the proof of its authenticity being displayed in the roughly cut initials "Y.P.," evidently the work of Bonnie Prince Charlie himself, on the leather sheath.

Generally speaking, I think it may be assumed that no monarch ever slept in a room that was not built until he had been dead for a hundred years. Fifty years should be accepted as the minimum for such an incident. And the probabilities are that no relic of even the most easy-going sovereign should be accepted as authentic that was not made within at least ten years from the date of his or her death.

As for the legends of the member of the family who was known as "the wicked lord" or "Black Sir Ughtred," there is a tiresome sameness about them all, and most of them should be treated as overworn coins and called in. For instance, there is the story of the dreadfully wicked man of property—his portrait is usually in a panel over the fireplace in the hall—who provoked a neighbour of whom he was jealous to fight a duel with him after dinner one afternoon. They used pistols, taking aim across the table that bore the decanters and wineglasses, and the wicked gentleman shot his friend through the heart, but escaped the consequences of the fell deed by inducing his companions to announce to the world that the man had died simply of heart failure. The story is plausible enough, if you assume that the coroner and the sheriff and all the other authorities were three-bottle men, and it is easy to suppose that in the early eighteenth century such high officials might be so described; but there is no necessity to wind up the story by showing the visitor the mark that the bullet made in the linen-fold wainscoting of the dining-room. You see, that striking evidence of the scrupulous accuracy of the story makes it essential for you to believe that the fatal bullet passed through the worthy gentleman's heart and slued round his backbone before lodging in the woodwork behind him, and this is asking too much.

I do not suppose that there is a Parliamentary Division of any county in England that does not contain a mansion with a room in which this duel was fought. Upon one occasion I visited a lesser country house where I happened to know a duel had been fought in the dining-room in the eighteenth century. I did not venture to inquire of the owner if he had heard of that tragic incident: I did not believe that he had; but when I was examining a very spurious picture attributed to Canaletto, after admiring a dexterous forgery of a rocky landscape by Salvator Rosa, he drew my attention to a portrait of a "black-avised" gentleman in a wig, and the story of the historical duel came out at once.

"I must show you the panel in the dining-room that was splintered by the bullet," said my host; and though I did not insist, he kept his word.

"It is said," he continued, when I was looking at the imperfect woodwork, "that the fellow was so stricken with remorse that he would never allow the panel to be repaired, in order that he might be constantly reminded of his deed; and it's a tradition in our family that it is never to be repaired, so there it is to-day."

I did not make myself objectionable to the family by assuring them that they might send for the carpenter any time they pleased without offending the shades of their ancestors, for it so happened that that particular duel was fought with swords and not with pistols.

III.—FATE OF THE FAMILY PORTRAITS

I n connection with family traditions and family portraits there are bound to be some grimly humorous episodes with the lapse of time, owing to the exactions of those Chancellors of the Exchequer who have held office since the creation of the Death Duties, as they are called. When a man with no ready money of his own inherits an estate that has not paid its expenses for many years, and a splendid mansion containing about fifty pictures, which, according to the most recent auction-room prices, may be worth from £100,000 to £150,000—people at picture sales think in pounds and bid in guineas—the question that at once presents itself is how to meet the demands of Somerset House. The fortunate heir, without a penny in his pocket, is called on to hand over from £10,000 to £15,000, according to his relationship to the late owner, and he wonders how he is to do it. In some cases that have come under my notice the only feasible way out of the difficulty has been taken, and some of the pictures have been sold in order to pay for the privilege of retaining the others. In the case of some historical mansions, however, every picture in the gallery is perfectly well known to the world, and the heir has a good many more qualms about selling any of them than Charles Surface had about disposing of his collection, with the exception of "the little ill-looking fellow over the settee." He feels—if he is capable of any feeling at all—that he is selling his own flesh and blood, and he always wonders what people will say when they come to visit the historical house and find blank panels in which, for perhaps two or three hundred years, stately figures of men and graceful figures of women had appeared.

What is he to do in such circumstances, while he is thinking his thoughts on a settee in the hall, and the Chancellor of the Exchequer is pulling away like mad at the wrought-iron bell handle outside and telling the butler that his instructions are not to leave the place until his bill is paid?

It seems that there is only one way by which the honour of the family can be preserved. There are trusty agents who can negotiate for an immediate and a secret sale of certain of the pictures. These are taken out of their frames or out of their panels, copies are made and put where the originals had been for years, and when the latter are passed on to New York or Chicago, unsuspecting lovers of Art stand beneath copies in admiration of the power of the Masters!

That is how the honour of the great family remains untarnished, while the Chancellor of the Exchequer strikes a match on one of the stone columns of the porch, lights his cigarette, and goes jauntily down the avenue with a large cheque in his breast-pocket.

All very well this for the time being; but a little comedy may possibly take place some years later, when once again Death Duties have to be paid, and probably at an increased rate per cent. No note may have been made of the pictures that were sold, and the copies have been subjected to the admiration of visitors without a misgiving. There are, I happen to know, copyists of Sir Joshua Reynolds and others of Thomas Gainsborough, Romney, Raeburn, Lawrence, and the rest, of such skill in reproducing the style of their particular Master that only the cleverest connoisseur could say, after the lapse of a year or two, which are the originals and which the copies. How, then, is a valuation to be made when the new owner enters upon his inheritance?

I fancy that it will be discovered Masters than were suspected of it had made replicas of their greatest works, and shipped off one to Chicago while selling the other to the great English families who gave them the order a hundred years or so ago.

CHAPTER FIVE—THE COUNTY, OLD AND CRUSTED

I.   —THE STRANGERS

W HEN THE LATE MR. W. P. FRITH WAS AT the height of his fame, and engravings of his "Derby Day" and "The Railway Station" contested for prominence on the flowery flock-papered walls of many drawing-rooms with Landseers "Monarch of the Glen," he went to pay a visit to his daughter in a southern county, and she has placed it on record that when she mentioned his name to the leaders of Society in various localities it conveyed nothing to them.

Why should it convey anything to them? He did nothing but paint all his life. Fame in painting, in music, in writing, means nothing—in many cases rather less than nothing—to the society of any English county. If the man had brought down a couple of hunters and gone out three times a week to hounds, the people in his division of the county would talk to you of him and look on you with astonishment if his name conveyed nothing to you; and the wife of a retired country doctor who takes up what is known as Church work—organising village teas and village concerts and Sunday "Unions"—is at once accorded a position that counts as fame in such communities in England.

But if it were not for observing these features in country life nothing of its lighter side would be apparent. There is nothing so comical as a picture in which all the laws of perspective are ignored; and living in a country town in England is like placing oneself in the position of the man in Edgar Allan Poe's story who, looking out of his window, saw an immense and hideous monster—a thing with splay feet and a huge proboscis—stalking with mighty steps across a distant lawn, and was greatly perturbed until he discovered that the creature was only an ordinary sort of spider walking across one of the strands of its web, which was drawn across the window pane.

Every day one may have experience of people living in the midst of such distorted perspective—fancying that the commonplace insects that move before them are creatures of enormous proportions and importance, and quite as frequently assuming that because an object appears small to them, being far away from them, it is quite insignificant. If one cannot find humour in observing the attitude of people who ignore the conditions of perspective in this way, one must be stolid indeed.

A typical inhabitant complained to me very bitterly some time ago of having just discharged a very thankless duty in respect of a stranger who, at the instigation of his brother—a London barrister of some repute—had called upon him in motoring through the county. He admitted that the stranger was a nice enough sort of man, but wholly devoid of appreciation of the relative importance of the persons whose houses were pointed out to him from the summit of the old castle which the stranger had been anxious to visit.

"I showed him Lord Riverland's place—as much of it as we could see through the trees—but all he said was, 'Who is Lord Riverland?'" continued the man, pouring his complaint into my ear. "And then I told him that just beyond Eglam Church was the Shillingdales' place. 'Funny name, Shillingdale!' was all that he remarked; but when we were leaving the castle he saw the gable of Maxfield's house sticking out, and he took a fancy to that tumbledown place and asked who lived there. I told him. 'Maxfield,' he said. 'Not Laurence Maxfield, I suppose?' I said that I believed his name was Laurence. 'What! Laurence Max-field, the painter?' Yes, I said, I heard he was something in that line. Well, you should have seen his face at that. 'How can I ever thank you sufficiently for pointing out that house to me?' he cried. And when we got down to the road he kept hovering about that place, and once he said, 'What kind fate led me here to-day? And yet I might have gone away without so much as glancing at the house of Laurence Max-field!' Now, is it any wonder that I almost lost my temper? I had pointed out to the fellow Riverland Park and Shillingdale Hall, and yet I don't believe he ever heard of Lord Riverland, or knew that Captain Shillingdale had been made a D.L. for the county! But he almost became maudlin over the two old cottages that Maxfield knocked into one! A painter! The idea of making a fuss over a painter!"

"You forget that the man was a total stranger to our neighbourhood," said I. "You must make allowances: he knew no better."

He said he supposed the fellow really did know no better; and I am convinced that in his own way he abused his visitor to his wife for the man's deplorable lack of all sense of proportion, to ignore the privilege of having a distant view of the mansion of a deputy-lieutenant of an English county and feasting his eyes on the cottage of a painter!

II.—THE INSECT AND THE MAMMOTH

A more amusing example still of the insect being taken for the mammoth was given to me by the person whose mammoth-like proportions (intellectually) were neglected because all eyes were directed upon the passage of an insignificant local insect across the line of vision.

He was a literary man whose name is known and respected in every part of the world—not merely in that narrow republic known as the world of letters. He was staying for a week at the house of a friend, when a lady, who was getting up a charity concert at Ringdon, calling at the house one day, and being told in a whisper by one of the daughters of the family when walking through the garden that they had a celebrity with them, entreated him to "do" something for the entertainment of her audience: she didn't mind what it might be that he would do, if he only agreed to do something.

Now it so happened that the lady had a more potent qualification than persistence in making an appeal to a man—she was extremely good-looking —and the man could not resist her importunity. He pro-mised to tell some short stories at the concert, and, in accordance with the terms of his promise, he turned up in the schoolhouse where the concert was to take place, supported by his host and two of the family. But the charming lady had not mentioned the fact that the entertainment was to supplement a parochial tea, and when they arrived this part of the programme was scarcely over. There were no printed programmes; only the clergyman who presided had before him a list of the performers and the nature of their performances, and he at once called upon a young woman who played very prettily on the piano. A young man, who professionally was the assistant to the Ringdon baker, was then called upon to sing the "Death of Nelson," which he did without faltering. When the applause had died away the clergyman rose from his chair and said—

"My dear friends, we have with us this evening a gentleman who has very kindly consented to contribute to our entertainment. He is a gentleman with whose name you will all be familiar. Were he not present I should like to refer more particularly to his honourable career; for in his presence I feel that it would not be good taste to do so, and, besides, he is so modest that I know he would be set blushing even though I were only to say one-half of all that was his due. My dear friends, I call upon you to give a hearty welcome to Mr. Reuben Robinson, who has come all the way from Netherham to give you his entertainment familiar to you all, I am sure, under the title of 'Charlie and

Charlotte.'"

The amateur ventriloquist went on the platform with his horrid puppets, and the young people cheered him for several minutes.

Later in the evening the clergyman, without any preliminary discourse, called upon the literary celebrity to tell his stories. Now throughout the world this writer is known as Alec Bidford, and now for the first time in his life he heard himself alluded to as Alexander Bedford; and it became clear to him that the good clergyman had never heard his name before!

Happily the victim of the beautiful lady's importunity has a keen sense of humour, as any one who goes farther than the parson did, and reads one of his books, will not need to be told, and I have never heard him more humorous than when he refers to his selfconsciousness while the clergyman was dealing with the fame achieved by—Mr. Reuben Robinson, the amateur ventriloquist, who had come all the way miles from the village of Netherham, where he sold bacon in the daytime. I do not know what Alec Bid-ford's opinion is, but I do know that there are some people who believe that this sort of discipline is good for one, whether one may be a literary celebrity or some lesser personage. An appearance in a Court of Law usually serves the same purpose; but it must be more than irritating to a man whose name is known to and honoured by every member of his own profession to be treated in the court with no more consideration than is extended to the merest nonentity. The judge professes never to have heard his name mentioned before, and, if he has been a witness, refers to his evidence without thinking it necessary to give him the ordinary prefix of "Mr." I have seen six of the most distinguished literary men in England—popular men, too, as well as geniuses—give evidence in a Court of Law, and yet the calling out of name after name did not cause even one of the solicitors' clerks to raise his head from the paper which he was reading, and the jurymen chatted together without being in the smallest degree impressed by the prospect of hearing the great one's voice.

This also is discipline, I suppose. At any rate, it suggests that a provincial town is not the only place where a sense of proportion is lacking.

CHAPTER SIX—THE OLD COUNTY TOWN

I.   —IN THE HIGH STREET

I F OUR THURSWELL IS A TYPICAL English village, assuredly Mallingham is a typical country town, only inclining to the picturesque side rather than the sordid. Like most picturesque towns, it is more highly appreciated by strangers than by its own inhabitants. Its one long street crawls along a ridge of the Downs, and from the lower level of the road that skirts this ridge and meanders among fat farms and luscious meadows, with an old Norman church here and there embowered in immemorial elms and granges mentioned in *Domesday Book*, steep lanes of old houses climb to the business street. It is really impossible to reach the town without a climb of some sort; and this fact, which made the site an ideal one, from the standpoint of the mediaeval founders of its walls and gates, remnants of which may yet be discovered by any one searching for them in a true archaeological spirit, causes a good deal of grumbling among the residents on both levels, who have to face many climbs in the course of an ordinary day's work. But motoring strangers, who pass through the town by the hundred every day, travelling between the two fashionable coast resorts, glance down the narrow lanes and say, "How simply lovely!" or "Doesn't it remind you of Nuremberg?" Perhaps it does remind them of Nuremberg—I have known people who affected to be reminded of Sorrento at Brighton—but for my part Mallingham only reminds me of an English country town, the convenient centre for a ten-mile area of villages. Enough business is done in its properly called High Street to allow of two banks keeping their doors open, and of half a dozen shopkeepers making modest fortunes in the course of a hundred years or so, and retiring from their half-timbered places of business to the avenue of red brick villas with well fires and radiators which an enterprising "developer" of one of the manors perceived to be a long-felt want. But the shops go on from generation to generation with the old names over the front, and in many cases with the family of the new generation living on the premises in the good old way. Only in this sense, however, may the tradesmen be said to be "above their business"; there is not the least disposition on the part of any of them to appear anything beyond what they are, for the simple reason that they do not think that the world holds anything better than a Mallingham tradesman. And, indeed, I am not sure that the world holds anything less ambitious. The aspirations of most of them do not go beyond the acquiring of a plate-glass frontage. Occasionally this dream literally crystallises, and when the crates are known to be actually awaiting delivery at the Goods Station, the "consignee" of the waybill is pointed out to strangers by the simple casement shopkeepers with bated breath and an occasional break in the voice. It is understood that the plate-glass front can only be achieved by a limited number of traders, and for years it was accounted a gross piece of presumption for any one whose lineage as a shopkeeper could not be traced through at least three generations of bill-heads to make a move in the direction of a "front"; but just before last Christmas a bolt from the blue fell upon the astonished town, for the two demure old ladies who kept a small millinery shop (with gloves and table linen at the farther end) put up bills on their small latticed window announcing a cheap sale in consequence of "impending alterations." Now that particular shop front had remained unchanged for certainly a hundred and fifty years—perhaps two hundred and fifty years—and the two old maiden ladies who had looked after it for close upon half a century seemed the most conservative of persons, so it was taken for granted that the alterations which were "impending" had reference only to the affixing of a new sun-blind in good time for the summer, or perhaps an outside lamp to make the winter nights more cheerful.

After a considerable amount of discussion on the subject an informal deputation waited upon the ladies to obtain information on a matter which, it was understood, affected the well-being of the whole community, and which was approaching a stage when a specific pronouncement one way or another was absolutely necessary.

Then it was that the truth was revealed. The maiden ladies had, they confessed, been surreptitiously discussing the putting in of a plate-glass front, and they had come to the conclusion that as they were both old and life at best was uncertain, they should not any longer procrastinate the carrying out of a scheme which the growth of the town and its increasing importance fully warranted, they thought.

It took just four days to fix the new front in its place; but it was the topic of the town for months, and even now you will see an occasional group of town people discussing the innovation and wondering what things are coming to.

The dimensions of the topic were, as I ascertained for my own satisfaction, nine feet broad by seven feet high. This was the *premier pas*. It led to the extravagance of a sunk letter sign, picked out in gold, an outside lamp, and a spring sun-blind, all of the most conventional pattern, and all to my mind in the condition of the "party in a parlour" in the Wordsworth parody. In short, a charming old house with many features of interest was transformed into a foolish hybrid thing—a single sheet of plate-glass on the ground floor, beneath two pairs of small cottage casements with delightful stone eaves. So prosperity turns out the picturesque or, at least, relegates it to the basement, and so a street with all the charm of past centuries clinging to it is fast becoming commonplace, and strangers driving through it laugh at the feeble attempts to give the commercial air of Harrods to a row of cottages—about as sensible a proceeding as it would be to attempt to assimilate the façade of Hampton Court with that of Hampton's in Pall Mall.

Happily there are still some sixteenth-century eaves left and also some eighteenth-century bow windows—the gentle curved bow of the eighteenth century, not the detestable obtuse-angle things of the mid-nineteenth—and happily the spirit of commercial enterprise does not pervade the entire community. Several of the houses that have been turned into shops contain admirable chimneypieces and panelled rooms, with an occasional fire-back and basket grate. It seems, too, that there must have lived in the place a century or so ago a master workman with a great fancy for decorating chimneypieces after the style of Adam; for in many of the rooms of sixteenth-century houses may be found quite good examples of the early style of Robert Adam. In one house there is a fine parlour decorated throughout in this way.

II.   —PRECIOUS PANELLING

Some time ago a mason, while doing some repairs in a room in a very old timbered house, disclosed some oak panelling which probably belonged to the sixteenth century. The news of the discovery went abroad, and a collector of "antiques" in the neighbourhood bought the woodwork for a hundred pounds —far more than it was worth, of course, but that is nothing; the effect of the find and of the sale was disastrous to the occupants of other old houses, for they forthwith summoned masons and carpenters and began pulling down their walls, feeling sure that a hundred pounds' worth of panelling was within their reach. They were all disappointed; for several years had passed before the landlord of the chief hotel—it had once been the county town house of a great local family—found behind the battens which served as the stretchers of the canvas that bore some very common paper in his coffee-room, a long range of oak wainscoting covered with paint. The usual local antiquary made his appearance, and through dilating upon its beauty and abusing the vandalism that had spread those coats of paint upon the oak, induced the landlord to give the order to have the panels "stripped" and made good. He little knew what he had let himself in for! The carpenters and the painters attacked the room with spirit (of turpentine), and for weeks it remained in their hands; for it was found that at least twenty coats of paint were upon the woodwork, and that a great portion of it was only held together by the paint, so that with the removal of this binding medium the panels became splinters.

Before the end of a profitless six weeks the good landlord was wishing with all his heart that that relic of a bygone period had been allowed to rest comfortably buried beneath the papered canvas that had entombed it all. The bill that he had to pay for the restoration was for such a sum as would have been sufficient to buy the same quantity of absolutely new panelling, he explained to some people to whom he went for sympathy! He laid great stress upon the fact that he could actually have got new panelling for the price of repairing the old!

"HE COULD HAVE GOT NEW PANELLING FOR THE PRICE"

And this was the spirit in which a far-seeing but non-antiquarian lady, who lived in another ancient house in the same street, received the liberal offer of a gentleman from the United States who had taken a fancy to her oak staircase. It was a commonplace type and might be found by the dozen in any old town; but he told her that he would pay her a hundred pounds for it, and she jumped at his offer. The staircase was carted away and a new one of serviceable deal, absolutely fresh from the carpenter's shop, was put in its place.

Her example induced a relation of hers—also a maiden approaching the venerable stage—to sell the panelling of one room, the fireplace of another, the Georgian pillared cupboards of a third, and actually the old black and white slabs of the square hall. Hearing of all this selling going on, an enthusiast made her an offer for the pillared porch of the house, and another for the leaden cistern on the roof and the copper rain-water head. Last of all, a man who was building a house in imitation of the old in the neighbourhood set covetous eyes upon her twisted chimney-pots and some peculiar coping tiles on the roof. She accepted every offer—with modifications; but when she had fulfilled her part of the business she found herself a solitary figure amid the ruin of a nice house, but with a nice little sum in her pocket. It was at this juncture that an enterprising tradesman from Brindlington, who was on the look out for "branches," came upon the half-dismantled house. Thinking that it was about to be pulled down, he made inquiries about it, and these he considered so satisfactory that he bought, at a good price, all that the previous speculators had left of it, completed their work of demolition, and within six months had erected upon the site some "desirable business premises" in the cheapest red brick, with an inconceivable broad expanse of plate-glass which he called somebody's "Co-operative Stores." He had co-operated with so many people in carrying out the work of destruction in regard to the old premises, it seemed only fit that the same principle should be maintained in their reconstruction. The place is only a branch establishment, but it is said to be flourishing as well as the parent tree.

III.—THE AMENITIES OF THE HIGH STREET

Every here and there between the shops in the High Street is a house that has survived the request—it never amounts to a demand in Mallingham—for "business premises." Quite unpretentious is the appearance of all these houses, but the front door opens upon a hall that is a hall, and not a mere passage to a narrow staircase. Admirably proportioned rooms are to be found on every floor, and usually a door at the farther end of the hall admits one to a garden, and not a mere patch of green. Here are gardens that have been cultivated for hundreds of years and so artfully designed that each of them has the appearance of a park, with lawns, and terraces, and pergolas. Here, not thirty feet back from the street, are acres of orchard, with mulberry trees of the original stock introduced by James I. to make possible his scheme of English silk weaving. The arbutus has also a home in several of these surprising pleasure grounds, with several other rare but fully acclimatised flowering shrubs. Shady walks among giant lilacs and laburnums lead to banks of roses and beds of lilies, and hardy borders of brilliant colour such as a stranger could never fancy might be found in so unpromising a region.

The lucky residents in these wonderful houses are usually extremely exclusive—if they were not so, goodness only knows what might happen. When a lady of good family finds herself living next door to a grocer and an ironmonger, she is bound to take steps to prevent the possibility of any one fancying that she belongs to that *galère*, and the steps that some of them take with this fact in their mind are sometimes very diverting. They usually assume the form of ignoring the existence, not so much of the grocer and the ironmonger as of the other ladies similarly situated. If you call upon Miss Wheatly at No. 10 High Street and, after praising up her garden, refer to the garden of Miss Keightley at No. 20, Miss Wheatley will express great interest, saying she has often heard that Miss Keightley's garden is quite charming, but she has never seen it for herself. Miss Keightley on her side may go even further, and not merely pretend that she has never heard of Miss Wheatley's garden, but also that she had no idea that any one named Wheatley lived in the town. This is at first, but she occasionally betrays a scrupulous anxiety to be accurate by asking, "What did you say the name was? Wheatley? Oh yes, to be sure I remember hearing the other day that a Miss Wheatley lived at No. 10. And you say she has a nice garden?"

And these good ladies may have been living within a few doors of one another for forty odd years, and the father of the one may have been in the butter trade, while the father of the other was in eggs.

The social distinctions in a country town such as Mallingham are sometimes very pathetic. It might be thought that the people would find a bond of union in that illiteracy which they enjoy in common, or in that profound ignorance of everything connected, however distantly, with art or science in which they live from one end of the year to the other; but one does not find it so. Mallingham is perhaps the most ill-informed town in England on all matters pertaining to culture, whether literary or artistic. A stranger who was unacquainted with this fact thought he was scoring a point in a speech which he had been called on to make in the absence of the Member for the Division at the annual banquet of the Barham Trust—the most important incident of the winter in Mallingham—when he remarked that he felt that the town must be the centre of the greatest literary activity; for, motoring through the High Street, he found on one of the shop signs the name Swift, on another the name Smollett, a little farther on he came upon an Addison (great applause), and finally he found himself close to the house of Hume. Surely, he said, these names spoke for themselves.

They had need to, for none of the élite of Mailingham could speak for any of them, except Addison, for Mr. Addison was a pork butcher, who the day before had been elected a member of the Corporation, after a hard struggle with a saddler. It so happened that the bearers of all the other literary names were not applaudable people—two of them were definitely unpopular—but the name of Mr. Addison was received with cheers, not by reason of his connection with *The Spectator*, but simply because of his recent achievement, and no one at the banquet had the least idea what the orator was referring to in bringing forward that string of names. "He might surely have mentioned Mr. Fawley, who was twice Mayor, or George Hanson, who has just bought the saw mills," a prominent burgess remarked to me when I was in his shop the next day. "But what has Peter Swift done, or Tom Smollett, or even Walter Hume? Decent enough men, I don't deny, but out of place when named in prominence at the Barham Banquet."

I never met anyone in the town who had heard these names in any other connection than that of Mailingham shopkeepers.

Some time later a new curate at St Bartholomew's, when proposing a vote of thanks to the chairman of one of his social meetings (with a magic lantern and an amateur ventriloquist), became erudite and droll by referring to "what Dr. Johnson said about music." The next day one of the churchwardens—a land agent—asked him how on earth he could attribute such a sentiment to Dr. Johnson. "I knew Dr. Johnson as well as most people, and there never was a man in the town who enjoyed a song better or knew better what a good song was," he said; and when the perplexed curate recovered himself sufficiently to be able to explain that there was another Dr. Johnson who said things besides the person of the same name who had once enjoyed quite a large and lucrative practice as a fully qualified veterinary surgeon at Mallingham, the churchwarden smiled and shook his head. "As much as to say," the clergyman added in telling me the story—"as much as to say that my excuse was far from plausible, but that he would accept it to prevent the matter going farther."

That narrative I found to be beautifully typical of the literary erudition of Mallingham.

IV.   —THE TWO ICONOCLASTS

Some four or five miles away are the imposing ruins of a great abbey of the Franciscans. It had once been of so great importance in the land that when the archabbey wrecker decreed that it should be demolished, he sent his most trustworthy housebreaker to carry out his orders. Now everybody of education in Mallingham can tell you all that is known about the venerable ruin, and it is the pride of the town that it should be so closely connected with the history of the Abbey; but I have never yet met with any layman in the neighbourhood who was not under the impression that the crime of its destruction should be added to the pretty long account of that Cromwell who was called Oliver, and I should not like to be the person who would suggest that there was another Cromwell—one who did not decapitate his king, but whom his king decapitated.

For that matter, however, it must be acknowledged that the people of Mallingham do not stand alone in mixing up those iconoclasts. I have found that in many parts of England as well as Ireland every deficiency in the features of a church figure or a church ornament is attributed to the later Cromwell. In Ireland I have had pointed out to me by clergymen of both churches the headless saints and the broken carvings caused by the fury of "Cromwell," though I knew perfectly well that the work of sacrilege could not have been done by him, for two reasons, the first being that in his devastating progress through Ireland he had never approached the places in question, and the second being that the sacred buildings in which the damage was done had not been built until long after Cromwell had sailed for England, after being soundly-beaten at Clonmel.

Of course in Ireland there was only one "curse of Cromwell"; but in England I soon found that there were two, and so the progress of confusion began, until at the present time, when you are visiting any old church and see in a niche an adult saint with a broken nose, or a carved rood screen deficient about the rood, the verger—sometimes the rector himself—is quite fluent in explaining that the heavy hand of Cromwell must be held accountable for the spoliation. If you ask which of the two, the answer will most certainly be, "Why, Cromwell to be sure—Cromwell—Oliver Cromwell."

An outsider should not interfere. The shade of Oliver would not shudder, even if such an expression of emotion were permitted the shadiest of shades, at the accusation being directed against him instead of the older Cromwell. He would probably say, if speech were allowed to him, "I have the greatest possible satisfaction in allowing my name to be associated with any act of iconoclasm of the nature of those acts so conscientiously perpetrated by my distinguished countryman."

He would feel that, could he have had any hand in smashing in the roofs of monasteries and despoiling rich abbeys, it would be accounted to him for righteousness. After such splendid acts of spoliation, knocking the nose off a poorly carved saint could not but seem a paltry thing, quite unworthy of any man with a reputation for a heavy hand to maintain.

But Mallingham, for all its literary and historical ignorance, has its heart in the right place; and it is staunch to Church and State—staunch to the core. Every Fifth of November it has its procession emblematic of these principles, and it must be confessed that the symbolism of the movement is not exclusive. To express adequately the loyalty of Mallingham, it is found necessary to set forth in marching order Turks, male and female, Negroes, Zulus, Toreadors, Pierrots, Harlequins, the Archbishop of Canterbury, Pirates, Mary Queen of Scots, Firemen, Dragoons, William Shakespeare, a Sailor, and many other characters, all of whom, it must be taken for granted, typify the triumph of Loyalty. Should any question a-rise—for captious inquirers may always be reckoned on in these days of high educational achievement—as to the identity of the leading typical figure in this pageant and the reason of the obloquy that is heaped upon him, culminating in the stake, with foul-mouthed explosives, the answer is that he is one Guy Fox, and that he is paying the penalty of having failed to blow up the Houses of Parliament. After that explanation no one can doubt that, whoever he was, he richly deserves his fate —or should it be spelt *fête?*

Occasionally co-opted with him is an unpopular person of distinction in the neighbourhood—a clergyman who lies under the stigma of preaching toleration, a police superintendent with a constitutional distaste for bonfires and low-flash explosives in the public streets, or perhaps a District Visitor suspected of "leanings." But usually by midnight the worst is over, and good nature without intoxicants prevails throughout the motley crowd; the Archbishop of Canterbury lights his cigarette—one of the packet with the pictures—from that of the Pirate King; Mary Queen of Scots hurries to the house where she discharges the duties of parlour-maid, complaining to a sympathetic Shakespeare that she has to be up at six in the morning to let in the sweep, and so home to bed.

The only literary fact which is impressed upon all the townspeople is that by some way never made quite clear, the singeing effigy, whose obsequies have been so imposing, was responsible for a *Book of Martyrs*. The general idea is that he was responsible for the martyrs themselves, and that Foxes

Book of Martyrs is a sort of catalogue with descriptive text of his victims.

So, as has been stated, the two Cromwells have but a single identity in the minds of Mallingham.

V. —THE SOCIAL "SETS"

Of course there is in Mallingham, as in every other country town, a first set and a second set—perhaps even a third, but that must be very close indeed to the unclassed tradesmen set, which is no set at all. And here it may be mentioned that the tradesmen's families are, as a rule, very much more refined and almost invariably better educated than the families of the first or second sets. Some years ago there was an amateur performance of one of Mr. Sutro's delightful plays given in aid of some deserving charity. Charity performances cover, as does Charity itself, a multitude of sins, but the leading lady did not need to make any appeal for leniency, so ably did she represent the part of the refined woman who was not quite sure whether she loved her husband or not. She was the daughter of a professional man, but had never succeeded in getting into the first set; for it must be remembered that there is no graduating from one set to another: one is either accepted or rejected at once. A couple of years later, however, the play was repeated, only this time it was under the highest patronage, so the management resolved to get the real thing. They managed to secure the services of a lady of title for the chief part, and the result was appalling. The refinement had vanished from the part, so had the correct pronunciation of the English language, so had the good taste in the toilettes worn, so had every vestige of intelligence. In place of these we were shown a pert young person with a voice like that of a barmaid in a country inn and a taste in dress to correspond. In the matter of memory for the words of the dialogue also the advantage was certainly on the side of the humbler representative of the part. In one of Mr. Henry James' most delightful short stories the catastrophe of "The Real Thing" is depicted. It was not more pronounced than that of the second representation of the comedy.

It is really very difficult to understand what are the qualifications for the best set in Mallingham; but somehow people usually find themselves in the set that suits them, and very seldom do the rulers of the social grades in Mallingham make a mistake. They have now and again sailed very close to the wind, however; for that was a nasty rub they got when they hastened to call upon a stranger, with the title of Baroness, who had taken a house in the new part of the town and kept a man-servant. As the story was told me, the ladies jammed one another in the doorway in their anxiety to be the first caller upon the Baroness, or Madame la Baronne, as the wife of a retired Indian civil servant called her, having studied the idioms of the *Comédie française*. Madame la Baronne was indeed a lady of great personal charm, and she was invited everywhere—even to the villa of the wife of the leading brewer, which represented a sort of Distinguished Strangers' Gallery in Mallingham. The competition among the most select for the presence of Madame at their houses was strenuous; and as she was in such demand it really should not have been regarded as so surprising that a London magistrate should send her a peremptory invitation by the hand of two detectives to come to the court over which he presided. His messengers would take no denial, he wanted her so badly, so she had perforce to throw over her local engagements and grant the magistrate the favour which he requested of her.

Her portrait was in the *Daily Mirror* the next day, in connection with a startling series of headlines, beginning, "The Bogus Baroness Again—Arrest at Mallingham." She was one of the most notorious swindlers that France ever returned to her native shore, after a series of exploits in Paris.

The ladies of Mallingham ran up against one another in the porch of her villa in their haste to get back the cards they had left upon her.

VI.   —THE CASE OF MR. STANWELL

That was what might be termed "a close call" upon the dignity and discrimination of the leaders of Society in Mallingham, and this was possibly why they held back when a man and his wife bearing the name Stanwell took a house in the town. The lady seemed quite nice and the man was passable, and before they had "settled down" it was noised abroad that they had a car: it need scarcely be said that to "have a car" is in country districts nowadays as sure a sign of respectability as "driving a gig" was in the 'thirties. There seemed to be no reason why these people should not be called upon by the leaders of Mallingham Society; but the leaders were getting more cautious than ever since the Baroness' scandal, and they hung back, none of them wishing to take a step which it would be impossible to recall, and every day the question of to call or not to call was informally discussed. It was just at this critical moment, when the fate of the Stanwells was trembling in the balance, so to speak, that one of the leaders was visited by a London friend, and on the name Stanwell being mentioned, this person asked, "Is that Herbert Stanwell, the author? It must be. I heard that he was leaving London and going to live in the country. They are all going. Soon we shall not have an author left in London; though I remember the time when they all lived there."

"This Mr. Stanwell has a car, I hear," was the "feeling" suggestion made by the Mallingham lady.

"So has Herbert Stanwell—he has been photographed in it dozens of times. Dear me! To think of Herbert Stanwell coming down here!" was the exclamation of the visitor; and the moment that she had gone back to London her hostess rushed round to her partners in the government of social Mallingham, and breathlessly announced that she had discovered that Mr. Stanwell was an author and that Mrs. Stanwell was his wife.

"Good heavens!" was the whispered exclamation from the syndicate. "Who would have believed it? And we were actually thinking of calling upon them! And they look quite respectable."

"And have a car!"

"Car, or no car, what I tell you is the truth. Is he not 'H. Stanwell?' and the authors name is Herbert. There's no doubt about it. And my friend, who knows everybody in London, said that Herbert Stanwell was about to live in the country."

She assumed the pose of a Princess Hohenstïel Schwangau, saviour of

Society, and she and her friends talked of how providential were certain incidents, let scoffers say what they might; for if she had not by the merest accident—ah, a providential accident!—mentioned the name of the Stanwells, no one would have known anything about them, and they might have been visited quite in good faith.

They parted, feeling that Providence was, very properly, mindful of the best interests of Mallingham; and so it was decreed that the newcomers—that pair who had made the attempt to get within the citadel of Mallingham's exclusiveness, not storming it boldly, but by the insidious device of concealing the fact that at least one of them was the author of over twenty novels—were not to be called on, although they had a car.

Before a month had passed, however, *The Happy Home*, a magazine widely circulated at Mallingham on account of its admirable paper patterns, contained an interview with Herbert Wilfred Stanwell, giving an excellent protrait of the distinguished author sitting (as usual) in his motor-car, with his favourite Chow, *Ming*, beside him; and the "letterpress" stated that he was unmarried, and that he had just taken a charming cottage at Henley (illustrated), on the lawn of which (illustrated), it might be taken for granted, all that was illustrious in Literature, Art, and the Drama would be found at week-ends during the summer, Mr. Stanwell's hospitality being proverbial.

The next day cards were left upon Mr. H. Stanwell and his wife, and it was universally admitted that they formed quite a congenial addition to Mailingham Society. He was a pleasant man and she was a charming woman. They came to Mallingham with a clean bill of health. Neither of them had done anything in the world, and the only time their names had appeared in the newspapers was when they had been married. They were nonentities to their finger-tips, and they soon took a high place among the nonentities of Mallingham.

Mr. Stanwell sorrowfully admits that more than once he has been asked in hotels in France and Italy if he was any relation to Herbert Stanwell, the great author. It is very annoying, he says, but he hopes to live it down. If he continues to live at Mallingham, he may be assured that his hopes run every chance of being realised.

It is greatly to be feared that the leading "note" of Mallingham is not literature. It is Thurswell that occasionally lays claim to be a great reading centre. It was in the most friendly spirit of honest patronage that a lady addressed a letter to George Eliot, commending some of the characters in *The Mill on the Floss*, but regretting that the story had not a happy ending.

"But it never reached him," she said. "I had sent it under cover to the publishers, but they returned it to me, with a scrawl across it, evidently done by a clerk, saying, '*Present address of* George Eliot not known, so, after all my trouble, it never reached him.''

Having mentioned *The Mill on the Floss*, I feel bound to say that neither in Thurswell nor Mallingham did the sporting innkeeper live who, on seeing a cheap edition of the book advertised, at once sent for it and read the greater part of it before he found out that he had been too hasty in taking for granted that it was written round a prizefight. A "mill" meant to him primarily such an incident, and his excursions into the magic realms of literature had practically been confined to the spirited accounts given incertain weekly papers of such encounters. A mill as an industrial building conveyed quite a secondary idea to him. He admitted to a friend of mine who found the book in the bar parlour, and wondered how it got he had been "had" over it, and his faith in the accuracy of literary advertisements got a severe jar. How was he to tell, he asked, that the chap meant another sort of mill?

How, indeed?

CHAPTER SEVEN—THE PEOPLE OF MALLINGHAM

I.   —THE MAYOR

ONE OF THE PECULIARITIES OF MALLINGHAM is the Mayor, for Mallingham has a Mayor all to itself, except when, by virtue of his office, he spends a happy day on various County Benches, joining with the representatives of local county families in the administration of Petty Sessions justice—Petty Sessions justice is founded on "good Crowner's Quest law"— otherwise he is usually a very worthy man, and lays no specious claim to popularity. He is never ostentatious or self-assertive, and in spite of the position which he occupies, he is in private life as sound an exponent of domestic virtue as if he were an ordinary simple citizen. The eminence to which he has risen never makes him lose his head or forget that kind hearts are more than coronets, and only very little inferior to a Mayoral Chain of office. It was the proud but very proper boast of a Mayor of Mallingham that although he had been proprietor of a provision business in the very centre of the town for over forty years, and had worn the chain for two consecutive terms, he was still just as approachable as any man in the kingdom.

Just as it was said in the Napoleonic days that every French soldier carried the *bâton* of a Field-Marshal in his knapsack, and as it is said in these days in the States that any citizen may one day become President—the contingency may account for the gloomy view so many American citizens take of life—so it is understood that any burgess of Mallingham may one day become Mayor. There is, however, no competition for the office, so unambitious are the majority of the burgesses; and now and again the Council find themselves face to face with the problem of how to induce any one to accept the chain of office.

Considering all that its acceptance entails upon the wearer, it can easily be understood that there should be some reluctance to have anything to do with it within the ranks of the eligible. If it were an understood thing that the burgesses of the town must buy their bacon and butter from the Mayor during his term of office, the problem of the Mayoralty might become less acute— assuming that a bacon and butter candidate were available; but no suggestion of this sort has ever been made so far as I can gather, and thus the difficulty is increasing year by year with the using up of all the available material for Mayors in the rough.

The fact is, that a great deal too much is expected from the Mayor. There is an inaugural banquet every year at which some two hundred burgesses, and several of the local gentry, and Members of Parliament, with a bishop, a rural dean, and an occasional chaplain to the forces, sit down on the invitation of the incoming Mayor.—He is expected to pay for everything, and as the feast is founded on the noblest traditions of civic catering, his bill cannot but be a heavy one. In no way is the menu inferior in interest to that to be found on the table of the Mansion House in the City of London. As a matter of fact, I believe that the turtle soup served at the Mallingham banquet is a trifle richer than that in the Mansion House, and the champagne is possibly a little sweeter. But the status of the large proportion of the guests at the one is widely different from that of the majority at the other. In Mallingham the tradesmen—gas-fitters, grocers, tobacconists, hair-cutters, newsagents, and the like—who are probably accustomed to a midday dinner of a cut from the joint, two vegetables, cheese, and a glass of ale, and want nothing better, work their way through a long and elaborate succession of dishes, between the *hors d'ouvres assortis* and the home-grown pineapple, drinking glass after glass of Ayala, *cuvée reservée*. Of course they may appreciate some of the simpler delicacies—*vol-au-vent* or the *faysans rotis*—but the most of the dishes are mysteries to them and, though very expensive, altogether obnoxious to the uneducated palate.

To be sure, the banquet is artfully meant: it is supposed to be by way of so incapacitating the diners that they are forced to listen to the speeches that follow. Only by the adoption of such stringent measures would it be possible to get a hearing for those speeches, made in all solemnity by the gentlemen at the High Table. A loyal Mayor has been known to spend twenty minutes over the Royal Family, after the King and Queen had been honoured—he took a quarter of over Their Majesties; but then the evening was comparatively young, and "The Bishops and Clergy of the Established Church," "The Clergy of other Denominations," "The Member of Parliament for the Division," "The Worshipful the Mayor," "The Corporation of Mallingham," "The Official Staff," "The Town and Trade of Mallingham"—all these had to be proposed and replied to in due course, and the general opinion was that in making up the accounts, with the banquet on the credit side and the speeches on the debit, a large balance remained against the Mayor.

And the inaugural banquet is merely the first of the series of entertainments which are supposed to come from the same source. Two or three balls, as many garden parties, and at least four large receptions, with refreshments, are looked for by the townspeople of all grades, for even the most exclusive of the leaders of the best set do not object to be entertained at the expense of the Mayor. They consider it their duty to attend the dances as well as the receptions; but there the transaction ends so far as they are concerned. They feel that they are honouring him by accepting his hospitality, and they do not consider that they are under the obligation to recognise him or his family if they meet in the public street, nor do they think it necessary to invite him or any member of his family to their houses. They really believe in their hearts that they lay the Mayor under an obligation to themselves by attending his receptions and his dances.

II.   —THE FIRST FAMILIES

That is the attitude of these good people whose names are quite unknown outside Mallingham. They are amusing through the entire lack on their part of a sense of comedy.

I am inclined to think, however, that the attitude of a son of one of these First Families, in respect of an incident that came under my notice, might be more definitely described. He had been invited by a man who was in a far better social position than himself to have a day with the partridges in a shooting which he leased; the youth accepted, and on the morning of the day named appeared in a dog-cart, bringing with him a friend with another gun. They passed the man who had given the invitation, and who was walking to the first field and had still a mile or so to go before reaching it; but though there was a vacant seat in the dog-cart he was not asked to take it. They drove gaily on, and did not even wait for him to come up with his dogs to begin operations. One of them was walking up one side of the field and the other was walking up the parallel side. The lessee of the shooting, on arriving, found himself taking rather a back place, the fact being that he had no acquaintance with his friend's friend, and his friend apparently not thinking it necessary to introduce him. The shoot went on, however, and, save for a little grumbling at the working of the dogs, it was successful enough. On getting round to the dog-cart, after walking through the last field, the visitors collected the birds that they had shot and tucked them under the back seat, and mounting to the front called out a cheery "good-bye" to the man who had entertained them. They were about to drive off, but the breaking strain of the other's politeness had been passed.

"I shouldn't mind a lift from you," he suggested.

"Sorry," explained the one with the reins; "but you see how rough the lane is, and really the machine is too heavy as it is. Ta-ta."

"On minute," said the pedestrian. "If it's too heavy I'll jolly soon remedy that," and he took a step to the dog-cart and pulled out the birds. "Pity you didn't think of that before. Now it's lighter. Off you go, and the next time you are offered a day's shooting you just inquire, from some one who knows, how you should behave. You will in that way be prevented from appearing a complete bounder."

For some time afterwards there was a sort of coldness between that man and the First Family, whose representative had been prevented by him from adding three brace of partridges to their menu for the next week.

For a plentiful lack of good manners the representatives of the "best set" in Mallingham could scarcely be surpassed in any community. The youth probably was quite sincere in his belief that he was conferring a conspicuous favour upon the man who had invited him to an afternoon among the partridges. How could it be expected that he should think differently when he had seen his mother and sisters feasting at the Mayoral ball one night, and cutting the Mayor the next day when they met him in the street?

It was not a Mayoress of Mallingham, but of a much more important municipality—one, in fact, of so great importance as to have a Lord Mayor and a Lady Mayoress—who had the privilege of entertaining a certain elderly offshoot of the Royal Family upon the occasion of the laying of the foundation-stone of a new hospital in the town. This particular minor Royalty is well known (in certain circles) for her ample appreciation of the dignity of her exalted position, and, like all such ladies, she is gracious in proportion to such dust of the earth as Mayoresses and Presidents of Colleges and Chairmen of Hospital Boards; and she made herself so pleasant to the Lady Mayoress who was entertaining her, that the latter determined to keep up the acquaintance, so she made it a point to pay her a visit in her private capacity. She drove up the stately avenue to the mansion, and inquired if Her Royal Highness were at home, just as if Her Royal Highness had been the wife of the vicar. She was admitted—as far as a certain room—and after an interval of long waiting there entered, not Her Royal Highness, but a stranger, a member of the "Household" of the minor Royalty, and they had a chilly chat together.

And the friendship so auspiciously begun at the opening of the municipal hospital made no advance beyond this interview, though it is understood that the lady of the Household was as polite as if she were Her Royal Highness herself.

III. —MISS LATIMER'S MARRIAGE LINES

There is nothing that the best set in Mallingham so resent as pretentiousness, or the semblance of pretentiousness, on the part of any one who does not belong to the best set. A few years ago a Mrs. Latimer, who lives in a delightful old house close to our village of Thurswell and is a widow, married one of her two pretty and accomplished daughters to a young man who was beginning to make a name for himself at the Bar. He had been at Uppingham and Oxford, and was altogether the sort of person by whose side the most fastidious young woman would not shrink from meeting her enemy in the Gate. The wedding was made an event of more than usual importance, for the girl and her mother were greatly liked, and on the mother's side were connections of actual county rank. The list of names in the county newspaper of the wedding guests and of the numerous presents was an imposing one: among the former was the widow of a Baronet, a County Court Judge, a Major-General (retired), and a Master of Hounds; and among the latter, a diamond and sapphire necklace (the gift of the bridegroom), a cheque (from the bride's uncle), a silver-mounted dressing-bag (from the bride's sister), and the usual silver-backed brushes, button-hooks, shoe-lifters, blotters, and nondescript articles. When the late Dr. Schliemann exhibited the result of his excavations at the supposed site of Troy, there were to be seen several articles to which no use could possibly be assigned. No one seemed to perceive that these must have been wedding presents.

It was, however, generally allowed that the wedding had been a very pretty one, that the bride had looked her best, and that the bridegroom appeared a good fellow; and in addition to the column and a half devoted to the affair by a generous newspaper, there appeared the usual announcement: Weston—Latimer.—On the 2nd inst., at Thurswell Church, by the Rev. Theophilas Watson, B.A.Oxon, Vicar of Thurswell, late Incumbent of St. Michael and All Angels, Bardswell, and Rural Dean, assisted by the Rev. Anselm Sigurd Mott, M. A., late Fellow of King's College, London, and Senior Curate of St. James the Less, Brindlington, William Henry, eldest son of the late John Weston of King's Elms, Leicestershire, to Ida Evelyn, elder daughter of the late George Cruikshank Latimer, of Todderwell, and Susan Prescott Latimer, of Grange Lodge, Thurswell.

This was the advertised notice in the *Telegraph*, as well as in the local paper, on the day after the wedding.

Three or four days later, however, there appeared, in the corresponding column of the *Post*, an amended version of the same announcement—Weston—Latimer.—On the 2nd inst., at Thurswell Parish Church, William Henry Weston, eldest son of the late John Weston, Attorney's Clerk, King's Elms, Leicestershire, to Ida, daughter of the late George C. Latimer, Farmer, Todderwell.

This piece of feline malevolence was easily traced to a lady with a highly marriageable daughter who had been posing for several years as one of the guardians of "exclusiveness" of Mallingham. An adroit lady had only to pay her a visit, ostensibly to call her attention to the delightful announcement—"the cleverest thing that had ever been done," she called it—to invite a return of confidence, and, with sparkling eyes, the perpetrator accepted the credit of thinking out the scheme for the humiliation of her neighbour for her arrogance in making so much of the wedding.

And the most melancholy part of the contemptible affair was that the greater number of the best set actually talked over it as a properly administered blow to the Latimers, and chuckled over it for many days.

But the very next year Mrs. Latimer's other daughter got married to the heir to a baronetcy; the wedding took place in St. George's, Hanover Square, and the *Post* gave an account of it to the extent of half a column, and the *Mirror* gave photographs of the bride and bridegroom.

It would scarcely be believed, except by some one acquainted with the best society at Mallingham, that upon this occasion the lady who had displayed her skill in snubbing the Latimers sent a two-guinea present to the bride. It was understood that the list of presents would appear in the *Post;* but when this list appeared the name of the donor of this special gift was absent from it: the two-guinea gift had been promptly returned by the mother of the bride.

And here is another touch: the valuable cake basket was returned with a heavy dinge in one place, which the jeweller affirms was not there when he packed it in tissue paper and shavings in its box with the card bearing the inscription: "To dear Constance, with best wishes from————" That is why he refused to take it back.

It was the son of this lady whose generosity was so spurned who, on leaving the rather second-class public school at which he received a sort of education, gravely said to another boy from Mallingham who had also just been finished—

"I suppose I'll often see you at Mallingham, old chap, as we are both living there, and I'm sure that I should be very glad to have a chat with you now and then; but, of course, you won't expect me to acknowledge you if I am walking with my mother or sister."

"Why not?" asked the other boy.

"Oh, my dear fellow, can't you see that it would never do?" said the first. "You know that your people are not in our set. You can't expect that because we happen to have been three years in the same house, we are in the same social position at home. But, as you know, there's nothing of the snob about me, and any time that we meet in one of the side streets, and even at the unfashionable end of High Street, I'll certainly nod to you. But that's the farthest that I can be expected to go."

The other boy certainly expected him to go very much farther even than the unfashionable end of the High Street, and ventured to delimitate the boundaries of the place, and to say a word or two respecting its climate and the fitness of his companions and all his family for a permanent residence there. Being a biggish lad, and enjoying a reputation for being opposed to peace at any price, he could express his inmost feelings without being deterred by any inconvenient reprisals.

The other did not even respond to his exuberance upon this occasion. He sulked in the corner of the railway carriage where the conversation took place, and he has been sulking ever since.

IV.—THE ENTERPRISE OF MALLINGHAM

I t was a gentleman who travelled in the latest styles in soft goods who was heard to affirm that Mallingham was not a town: it was a dormitory.

He doubtless spoke from the horizon line of soft goods, having in his eye certain of those firms who still do business in the concave side of ancient bay windows, and have not yet been lured on to fortnightly cheap sales behind a sheet of plate-glass. A commercial traveller takes some time to recover his selfrespect after importuning a possible client in the con-cavity of an eighteenth-century window of what was once a dainty parlour, but is now a dingy shop.

THE COMMERCIAL TRAVELLER

But, as a matter of fact, there is a deep and pellucid well of enterprise in the centre of commercial circles in Mallingham, and it only wants an occasional stir to irrigate the dead levels of the town. For instance, there is published by a stationer in the High Street the *Mallingham Almanac*, an annual work which gives a large amount of interesting information valuable to many persons in an agricultural district, such as the list of fair days in all the villages in the county, the hours of the rising and setting of the sun (of undoubted interest to farmers), the changes of the moon (also very important to have noted down to the very second), the equation of time from day to day (without which we could hardly get on at all), the time of high water at London Bridge, and the variation of the compass (indispensable to agriculturists). A graver note is, however, sounded in the pages devoted to prophecy, after the style of the ever veracious Francis Moore, where readers, born when Mercury was in the Fourth House, are warned against eating uncooked horse-chestnuts on a Friday, and the general public are told that as, in a certain month, Mars and Neptune are in opposition—perhaps it should be apposition—news will be published regarding the German Emperor.

Then there are pages given over wholly to poetry, like Ephraim and his idols.

The spirit of enterprise which flutters—I am afraid that I referred to it in an earlier paragraph in a way that suggested water which really does not flutter, —as a moth round a flame, round a good advertising medium in Mallingham, is shown by the pages of business cards scattered throughout the sheets of this almanac.

In his Address to his Subscribers which prefaces the last issue, the publisher, who is also the editor, recognises in a handsome way the support which he has received from his numerous advertisers and expresses the earnest hope that they may all, individually and collectively, find that their business will rapidly increase as a reward for their enterprise.

On the opposite page may be read the business cards of three undertakers.

Mallingham is certainly not a dormitory so far as the possibilities of trade are concerned. It may safely be said that every business house will undertake undertaking in all its branches and the removal of furniture. No matter how small may be the apparent connection between the business professed on the shop sign and the undertaking industry or the removal industry, you will find on inquiry the utmost willingness expressed to meet your wishes in either direction.

The qualification of a dealer in antiques to carry out such a contract is not immediately apparent, but it is certainly more apparent than that of an auctioneer; at least, if you need to be buried, it is not to an auctioneer you will go in the first instance. To be sure, if you read *Othello* carefully you will find that there is quite an intimate connection between "removals" and undertaking; but, as a rule, for business purposes each of the two trades is regarded as distinct from the other.

But in Mallingham you not only find them amalgamated, but both are run (decorously) in association with hardware, upholstery, blind-making, carpetbeating, life and fire assurance (not at all so extraordinary this last named), crockery, and soft goods. It is rumoured that the largest business in the "lines" referred to is in the hands of a rag and bone merchant and a dyer.

It is pleasant to be able to record that no one has yet been known to accept the suggestion of the pun in regard to the aptitude of the dyer in such a connection, and it is certain that Shakespeare himself would not have been able to resist the temptation. But Shakespeare has said many things that no one in Mallingham would care to invent or even to repeat.

One of the most notable instances of the professional enterprise of Mallingham was told to me by its victim. He was a clergyman, and the curate of one of the parishes. Now there are curates who are as fully qualified to discharge the duties of their calling as is a Rector, or even a Rural Dean: some of those whom we find in the country have "walked the hospitals," so to speak, having been for years labouring in the slums of a large town; but some are what might be termed only "first aid" men, and it was a "first aid" curate who, on taking up his duties in Mallingham, set about a zealous house-to-house visitation, being determined to become personally acquainted with every member of his flock.

He had already made some headway in the course he had mapped out for himself, and was becoming greatly liked for his sociability before he had reached the letter R in his visiting list, at the head of which was the name of Mr. Walter Ritchie, the dentist, a gentleman who, in addition to enjoying an excellent practice as a destructive rather than a constructive artist, was a good Churchman. It was between the hours of twelve and one that the zealous curate found it convenient to call upon him, and he was promptly shown into the waiting-room, where there was an elderly lady with a slightly swollen face studying the pages of a very soiled *Graphic* of three weeks old. Of her company he was, however, bereft within the space of a few minutes, and the *Graphic* was available for his entertainment for the next quarter of an hour. Then the maid returned and said that Mr. Ritchie would see him now, and he followed her across the passage and was shown into the usual operating room of the second-class practitioner of the country town.

Mr. Ritchie greeted him warmly and so volubly as saved the clergyman the need for introducing any of the professional inanities which are supposed to smooth the way to an honourable *rapprochement* be-ween a pastor and an unknown member of his pastorate. The parson had not really a word to say when Mr. Ritchie got upon the topic of teeth, and warned his visitor that he must be very careful in his use of the Mallingham water until he should get accustomed to it. It had an injurious effect upon the natural enamel of the teeth of the lower jaw, he said.

"I will explain to you what I mean, if you will kindly sit here," he added, pointing to the iron-framed chair, the shape of which expresses the most excruciating comfort to a dentist's clientele. The curate, wishing to be all things to all men, though he had no intention of being a dentist's "example," smiled and seated himself. In an instant Mr. Ritchie had him in his power; bending over him, he gently scraped away some of the "enamel" from one of his front teeth and, exhibiting a speck on the end of the steel scraper, explained the chemical changes which an unguarded use of the chalky water of the town supply would have upon that substance, though it made no difference to the secretions of the glands of the upper jaw.

This was very interesting and civil, if somewhat "shoppy," of Mr. Ritchie, the clergyman thought, and once more opened his mouth to allow of the dentist's obtaining a sample of the alkaline deposit to which he had alluded. But the moment his jaws were apart Mr. Ritchie made a sound as of a sudden indrawing of his breath.

"Ha, what have we here?" he cried. "Nasty, nasty! but not too far gone— no, I sincerely hope, not too far gone. One moment." He had inserted a little shield-shaped mirror in the curate's mouth and was pressing it gently against an upper tooth. "Ah yes, as I thought—a little stuffing will save it. Nerve exposed. You are quite right to come to me at once. A stitch in time, you know. It will hardly require any drilling—only at the rough edges."

The clergyman was not the man to protest against Mr. Ritchie's civilities. He admitted that the tooth had given him some trouble the previous year, but he had not thought it worth consulting a dentist about.

"That's the mistake that people make," said Mr. Ritchie mournfully. "They usually associate a visit to their dentist with some atrocity—some moments of agony—that was the result of the old tradition, dating back to John Leech's days. Of course, in those dark ages dentists did not exist, whereas now—— I think I would do well to do a little crown work between the tooth I am stopping and the next: the gap between the two is certain to work mischief before many months are over, and the back of the nearest molar has become so worn through the pressure of that overgrown one below it that, if not checked in time, it will break off with you some fine day. I'm glad that you came to me to-day. I will make a new man of you."

He had the little ingenious emery drill working away before the clergyman remembered that he had not come to pay a professional visit to the dentist—that is to say, he had meant that his visit should be a professional one so far as his own profession went, but not that it should be a professional one so far as the profession of the other man went. But it seemed to him that the dentist was fast approaching the moment when he, the dentist, would not be amenable to the *convenances* of the parochial visit, but would become completely absorbed in the *nuances* of dental science which every revolution of the emery drill seemed to be revealing. He could say nothing. He was in an unaccustomed posture for speech. He was lying in the steely embrace of that highly nickelised chair, with his face looking up to the ceiling—exactly the reverse of the attitude in which he felt so fluent every Sunday evening. With his head bending over the top of his pulpit, he felt that he was equal to explaining everything in heaven above or the earth beneath; but sprawling back, with his eyes on the ceiling, and a thing whizzing like a cockchafer in his mouth, he was incapable of protest, even when he had recovered himself sufficiently to feel that a protest might be judicious, if not actually effective.

He submitted.

For the next four weeks he was, off and on, in the hands of Mr. Ritchie. It seemed as he went on that he had not a really sound tooth in his head, though he told me, almost tearfully, that previously he had always prided himself on his excellent teeth.

"I think Mr. Ritchie went too far in the end," he added, recapitulating the main incidents of his indictment of the dentist. "I dare say a couple of my molars were showing signs of wear and tear, and so were all the better for being filled in properly; and it is quite likely that the gulf between the other two was the better for being bridged over—possibly a flake or two needed to be ground away from one of the grinders at the back—but I am sure that the time occupied in correcting some of the other irregularities which he perceived, but which had never caused me a moment's inconvenience, might have been better spent. I often thought so; but I said nothing until he calmly advised me to have six of my upper jaw painlessly extracted, apparently for no other reason than to show me how the new system of injecting cocaine, or something, worked, and that he could do what he called 'crown work' with the best dentists at Brindlington—then I thought it time to speak out, and I did speak out."

"And what did you say to him?" I inquired, for I longed to be put in touch with the phraseology of a "first aid" parson when speaking out.

"I didn't spare him: I told him just what I thought of him."

"And what did that amount to? Nothing grossly offensive, I hope."

"I wasn't careful of my words; I did not weigh them. If they sounded offensive to him I cannot help it."

"What did you say to him, as nearly as you can recollect? I'm rather a connoisseur of language and I may be able to relieve your mind, if you have any uneasiness on the subject of the man's feelings when you had done with him. What did you say to him?"

"I told him plainly that I thought he had gone too far; and now, looking at the whole transaction from a purely impersonal standpoint, I am not disposed to withdraw a single word of what I said. He did go too far—I honestly believe it. You will understand that it is not easy for one to take up an attitude of complete detachment in considering a matter such as this in all its bearings; but I think that I have disciplined myself sufficiently to be able to consider it in an unprejudiced spirit, and really I do believe that he went too far."

"If he did, you certainly did not," said I. "Has he sent you in his bill?"

"It is not his bill that matters—it only comes to £5, 11s. 6d. What I objected to was his implication that I had not a sound tooth in my head—I that have been accustomed during the past five years to crack nuts—not mere filberts, mind, but the sort that come from Brazil—at all the school feasts without the need for crackers! Just think of it! Oh yes, he certainly went too far."

I agreed with him; I had no idea that there was so much enterprise in all Mallingham.

The general idea that prevails in regard to Mallingham is that it has remained stagnant—except for its aspirations after plate-glass—during the past four or five hundred years of its existence. A dog of some sort lies asleep at midday under almost every shop window, and cats of all sorts may be seen crossing the High Street at almost any hour. That is how it comes that the town seems so charming to visitors, and to those of its inhabitants who are not engaged in business.

This being so, I was disposed to laugh at the sly humour of a man and his wife—they were Russian nobles who motored across from Brindlington to lunch with us at Thurswell—who said they had enjoyed the drive exceedingly, until they had come to Mallingham. "A horrid, rowdy place, like the East End of London on Saturday night," were the exact words those visitors employed, and I had actually begun to laugh at their ironical humour when I saw that they were meant to be in earnest. For some time I was in a state of perplexity; but then the truth suddenly flashed upon me: it was the day of the Mallingham Races—one of the three days of the year when the dogs are not allowed to sleep in the streets and when the cats remain indoors, when the High Street is for a full hour after the arrival of the train crowded with all that it disgorges, and when there is a stream of vehicles carrying to the picturesque racecourse on the Downs the usual supporters of the turf, with redfaced bookmakers and their "pitches," as objectionable a crew as may be encountered in the streets of any country town at any season.

It was clear that my friends had reached the High Street of Mallingham a few minutes after the arrival of the train, and not being aware of the exceptional circumstances which had galvanised the place into life for a brief twenty minutes, they had assumed that this was the normal aspect of the town! I did my best to remove from Mallingham the reproach of being the great centre of bustling life that it had seemed to these strangers; but I could see that I did not altogether succeed in convincing them that, except for four days out of the year, nothing happens in Mallingham—three days of races and one night of loyal revelry—for even the holding of the Assizes three times a year does not cause the town to awake from its immemorial repose. The trumpets sound as the judge drives up to the County Hall with a mounted escort, and the shopkeepers come to their doors and glance down the street; the sleeping dogs jump up and begin to bark in a half-hearted way, but settle themselves comfortably down again before the last note of the fanfare has passed away, and, except for an occasional glimpse of a man in a wig crossing the street to the hotel, the Assize week passes much the same as any other week of the uneventful year. Three hundred years have passed since anything happened in Mallingham, and then it was nothing worth talking about. One must go back seven hundred years to find the town the centre of an historical incident of importance.

But the rumour is that Messrs. Williamson & Rubble, drapers and outfitters, are about to have a new plate-glass front made for both their shops, with convex corners and roll-up shutters; so Mallingham marches onward from century to century—slowly.

CHAPTER EIGHT—THE PUSHING PROVINCIAL TOWN

I. —THE MODERN METHODS

THE MILD AND BASHFUL ENTERPRISE of Mallingham is made to
look ridiculous when contrasted with the unblushing business energy of
Burford, that bustling town of twenty thousand inhabitants at the farther end
of Nethershire. Burford lends itself as an awful example of what can be
accomplished by that dynamic element known as "push." It was born
picturesque, but has since become prosperous. Its Corporation has long ago
done away with all those features of interest to antiquarians which are
ineradicable in Mallington, however earnestly the ambitious Council of the
latter may labour for their annihilation; so although strangers knowing
something of the early history of Burford, come to it expecting to find it the
"dear old quaint place" of the girl with the camera, they bicycle away before
accepting the hospitality offered by the bill of fare displayed in the broad
windows of the double-fronted modern restaurant lately set up by Messrs.
Caterham & Co., of London, where the old conduit house, mentioned in the
guide-books, stood for centuries, in the High Street. The Corporation are, it is
rumoured, meditating the advisability of altering the name of the High Street
into the King's Parade. The sooner they make a move in this direction the
better it will be for all concerned; for undoubtedly, as the Mayor recently
pointed out, the town has passed out of the category of towns with a High
Street, and may claim to be admitted into the select circle of those with their
Royal Avenues and Princes' Promenades.

So why not make a bold step forward with King's Parade?

Why not indeed?

The invasion of Burford by Messrs. Caterham, with their score of little
marble tables and a choice of four dishes for luncheon, was equivalent to
putting the seal of modernity upon the old High Street; but its claim to
compete in its extent of plate-glass frontage with the most advanced centres
of business enterprise, was long ago proved by the establishment of Messrs.
Shenstone's fine "drapery emporium" (vide advertisements) on the site of the
old Castlegate Inn. It is said that even in the difficult matter of supplying
sables to suit all classes of customers this house can hold its own with any in
the trade.

A customer enters with an inquiry for a set of sables.

"Forward furs," the shopwalker commands—he actually is a full corporal
in the Territorials—and the lady finds herself confronted at the counter by a

young man with a Bond Street frock-coat and a Regent Street smile, who says
—

"Sables, madam? Certainly."

He leaves her for a few moments and returns with an armful of furs, which he displays, laying each piece over his arm and smoothing it down as if it were—well, a sort of cat.

"Price, madam?" He refers to a ticket. "Two hundred guineas, madam—all Russian. Something not quite so expensive? Certainly, madam." Once again he goes away and returns with another armful. "These are quite superior furs, madam. Real sable? Certainly, madam, real Musquash sable. Sixty-five pounds. Something cheaper, madam? Certainly. I have a very nice line of inexpensive sables that I think you will like." He beckons to a young lady farther up the counter, and she brings him a bundle of tawny skins, which he displays as before. "A very nice line, madam—very chaste and showy. Real sable? Oh, certainly—real electric sable, every piece. Price, madam? Nine guineas, including muff. Something cheaper still? Certainly, madam." He climbs up a small and handy ladder and lifts down a large pasteboard box full of furs. "These, madam—very tasteful—large amount of wear—sell a great number of these. Real sable? Certainly, madam, real rabbit sable, thirty-nine and eleven. Something rather less? Certainly, madam." He pulls down another box, takes off the lid, and exposes skins. "Nice lot these, madam, very highly thought of—largely worn in London this season. Real sable, madam? Certainly, madam—real ox-tail sable, ten and six the set. Shall we send them? Thank you. What name, please? Johnston—with the t? Thank you. And the next article, madam? Oh yes, this afternoon for certain."

That is the sort of business house you find in the High Street, Burford, in these days; so that there can hardly be a doubt that it is time the thoroughfare changed its name to King's Parade. If people want genuine ox-tail sables they will go to a King's Parade for it much more readily than they would to a High Street. But there is a deeper depth in sables that a customer can only reach in a Royal Avenue; this is the genuine charwoman's sable at three and eleven, muff included. Messrs. Shenstone & Co. are, however, select and conscientious; they will not sell you as the real article anything that will not bear the closest scrutiny, and their ox-tail sable marks the limit to which they will go. It may be foolish in these go-ahead days to have any scruples, but Messrs. Shenstone are ready to submit to any reproach rather than to give a customer, however humble, a misleading description of any article.

II.   —LIBRARIANS WHILE YOU WAIT

As a matter of course, Burford has a Public Library of its own. The Corporation had a chance of acquiring a library that had been in existence for some years: it had been built as a memorial to her husband by a wealthy lady in the neighbourhood, and it contained several thousand volumes of the "improving" sort which were so much in favour with fathers and mothers and uncles and aunts—in fact, with all manner of people except readers—fifty or sixty years ago. For purposes of a public library such a collection is absurd, and should have been consigned to one of the Corporation's rubbish carts without delay, together with its Encyclopaedias dated 1812. The books were, however, allowed to encumber the shelves, and there they remain unto this day, to assist in the culture of much that would interest an earnest bacteriologist. To the majority of the members of the Corporation, however, "a book's a book although there's nothing in it," and their "library" is packed with books and bacteria, both happily undisturbed for years.

Some time ago a charwoman with a husband was required to sweep the floors and put the daily papers in their proper frames, and so the Corporation advertised for a "librarian" and his wife, mentioning the "salary" at fifty pounds a year. But they did not add, as they might have done, "no knowledge of books required," and the consequence was that at the annual meeting of the Library Association the distinguished President referred to the advertisement with disparaging comments in respect of the "salary" offered to the "librarian." It was not likely that such a reflection upon the liberality of the Corporation of Burford would be allowed to go to the world with impunity, so a member who considered himself responsible for the advertisement and the fixing of the renumeration wrote to the papers, pointing out that caretaker's rooms were granted to the "librarian" in addition to his "salary," so that the Corporation were really munificent in their offer; but whether they were so or not, they could get plenty of people to discharge the duties of "librarian" on the conditions set down.

He was quite right. The applicants for the coveted post were numerous. They represented all the out-of-work men in the neighbourhood. Porters, jobbing gardeners, discharged soldiers with the rank of private, and the usual casuals applied, and the most eligible of these seemed to be an ex-soldier: "We should do all we can for old army men," said one of the Committee very properly, and so the old soldier stood at attention, saluted, and became a "librarian." The ability of the Corporation of Burford must be admired: they can make any man a librarian in five minutes; though the general opinion that prevails on the subject is that long years of careful training are needed to qualify even a man of good education for the post of librarian!

That is where the management of a matter that makes no appeal to the illiterate becomes a farce in the hands of such a body. What they wanted was a charwoman with a husband, not a librarian with a wife; but with traditional pomposity they must needs advertise for a "librarian" with a "salary." So far as I can gather, the caretaker can sweep out a library with any man; but if you ask for any particular book—well, he does his best. But a man may be an adept with brooms and yet a tyro with books. He is another of the things that are not what they seem at Burford.

THE LIBRARIAN'S WIFE

III.—ARCHÆOLOGICAL ENTERPRISE

There is quite a good Museum at Burford. It was formed, I believe, in the pre-Corporation days, and so it is under intelligent control. Local antiquities are represented with some attempt at completeness and classification, and its educational value would be very great if the people of the neighbourhood could be induced to give to it some of the time that they devote to football. A few years ago, however, an irresistible appeal was made to the culture of the town by the acquisition for the collections of a human hand from the Solomon Islands. As soon as it was understood that this treasure had just been added to those in the Museum there was a rush to see it, and thousands of persons paid their sixpences for a glance at it, and in the course of a day or two after its arrival it had become the topic of the place. If you had not seen it you were regarded as a complete outsider. It was considered a great hardship that visitors were not allowed to touch this exhibit; for, after all, a look at such an object is unsatisfactory—quite different from a hearty handshake. To shake such a hand would be satisfying, it was generally thought, and I have much pleasure in associating myself with such an expression of opinion. A little of it would satisfy any but the most grasping nature.

It was in this Museum that there reposed for years in one of its glass cases an interesting exhibit labelled "Fragment of ancient pottery, probably Saxon, effects of lead glazing still visible."

It was thought to be part of a pitcher, and some ingenious and imaginative antiquary had made an excellent drawing of the original vessel, showing the bulge in the body from which the piece had been broken. Many papers had been written about the fragment, some authorities contending that it was not of Saxon but Roman origin, and others that, as it had been found on a part of the coast which had at one time been covered by the sea, it was almost certain to be of Scandinavian origin: it had been on board one of the Norse pirate galleys that had harried the whole of the South Coast, and marks were pointed out along the edge which were said to be the traces of a rude decoration of Scandinavian design.

For years the controversy was carried on with a large display of learning on all sides, until one day a geologist of distinction visited the Museum, and announced that the specimen of pottery was a section of a human skull. A little examination and a comparison of the specimen with an ordinary human skull showed beyond the possibility of doubt that this view was the correct one, and the label was changed without delay. But when it became known that the Museum was in possession of part of a human skull, it was visited by hundreds of people all anxious to get a glimpse of so interesting an object, and if possible—but this was rather too much to hope for—to hold it in their hands; and for weeks the contents of other cases lay unnoticed. The broken skull was the real attraction.

It was an amazingly thick skull: if it had not been so thick it would probably not have led its original owner to forfeit it, but would have suggested to him a way of escape from those unfriendly persons who had deprived him of its use. But the owner would certainly have made a good show at an old election fight, or have reached a green old age in Tipperary.

I once saw on a shelf in the Museum a piece of old ironwork in the form of a rushlight holder. So it was labelled, and the date 1609 assigned to it. It was stated on the label that it was probably the work of a well-known ironworker of the neighbourhood in which it had been found. I ventured, however, to differ from this last suggestion, the fact being that this particular example of seventeenth-century ironwork was not made during that century or by that craftsman, but by a more crafty person during the latter years of the reign of Edward the Seventh. My reason for coming to this conclusion was not the result of the possession on my part of any special acquaintance with wrought-iron or the methods of the old workers, but simply because I had been present when the thing was in course of being forged—in both senses *forged*. The craftsman had been called away from his job suddenly, and when I entered his unostentatious forge there the thing was lying as he had left it, in an unfinished condition. Some days later I saw it among a heap of scrap iron of various sorts in his yard, and it rather took my fancy. I pulled it forth and asked the man if he had any idea what it was. He replied that, so far as he could remember, an antiquarian gentleman had told him that it was for holding a rushlight. I looked at it closely and said that I did not think it was old, and he replied that he didn't believe it to be very old either; but it wasn't a handsome thing anyway.

I threw it down and began to talk about other matters, and the next I saw of it was in the Museum above its neatly lettered label.

I told the craftsman where I had seen it, and he smiled.

"It seems that there are people who know more about these ancient old things than us, sir," he said. "A man that has a great fancy for his own opinion came round here shortly after you were here, and I could see that he had his eye on that thing, though it was lying among the scraps; and when he had talked long enough to put me off thinking that it had caught his eye, he picked it up and asked me what I would take for it. I told him half a sovereign, and he beat me down to three half-crowns. Then he sold it to Anson in the Cornmarket for a pound, and Anson took it to the Museum and got thirty-five shillings for it. That's the whole story. The others got a good bit more out of it than me."

"That was a shame," said I; "considering that you made it, you should have had the largest share of the profit."

He smiled and said—

"I don't complain. What would be the use?"

In the same neighbourhood there is another excellent workman. He has always in the backyard of his house quite a number of antique Sussex firebacks maturing. He lays down firebacks as wise people lay down wine to mature. They look absurdly clean and fresh when they come from the place where he casts them, but time and the oxide of iron soon remedy all those defects, and when they have been lying rusting for a month or two the aspect of the design is changed. A rough scrubbing—not too much, but just enough —and an exposure in a brisk fire to produce the marks of long years of duty in the sturdy old yeoman's grate, with the crane swinging over it, and another specimen of the Sussex fireback is ready for the market. The market is always ready. It will take the sturdy old yeoman's crane, with its hooks and its levers, as well as his fireback, and so the industry of the craftsman and the craft of the dealer man are stimulated.

There is still a brisk trade done in the manufacture of ancient flint weapons —hatchets, spear barbs, arrow-heads, and the like—in our county, though I have heard that there has been a melancholy falling off in the volume of business done in this particular line during the past twenty years. It is never well to be too certain about the treasures one acquires nowadays, either in iron or flaky flint, but I have heard that long ago a collector had quite as great reason to be cautious. A large number of interesting flint weapons were with reasonable luck to be dredged out of the sand and mud of some rivers. It was only reasonable to suppose that these things had some thousands of years ago been in active use in battles fought at the ford, and that they had remained undisturbed for centuries in the bed of the river. I heard of an eminent archaeologist having acquired quite a number of these implements bearing unmistakable signs of antiquity. They had been dredged out of the Thames from time to time, he heard. Unfortunately he mentioned this fact to a dealer who had also heard of these dredgings, and offered to lend him the collection for examination. The first experiment upon them was the last. They had only to be boiled in a strong solution of soda to have their true character—their false character—revealed. When taken out of the kettle the things were as fresh as if made the day before. They had not been made the day before, but they had certainly been made within the year. They were nothing more than flaky fakes.

After all, it is safer for a tradesman to use his own imagination in the preparation of his wares than to ask his customers to use theirs. For instance a dealer in curious things, in Burford, seeing some funny wooden dolls in a shop window, bought the whole five and then used up some scraps of old brocade and remnants of Genoa velvet in dressing them in costumes to be found in the recognised authority. He exposed them for sale sitting in a row, and very amazing they must have appeared.

"Quaint things, are they not? Mediaeval puppets. I don't know that I ever saw the like before. Of course you see what they are meant to represent? Why, the Five Senses, to be sure. Fifteen guineas for the five. If I don't sell them at once I'll send them to the Victoria and Albert Museum. They'll jump at them."

"I shouldn't mind buying one of them," said the customer; "but I could not do with the whole five."

"Sorry, sir; but you could scarcely ask me to break the set—I don't believe there is another set in existence," said the dealer.

"I think you might let me have one. I have bought a lot of things from you from time to time."

"I should like to, sir—yes, I should indeed like you to have one, but—you see the whole beauty of the set is that it is a set—the Five Senses."

Some further conversation ensued, and at last the dealer showed himself to be less inflexible than he had been at first, and the customer secured one of the mediaeval curiosities for four pounds.

A few days later another customer called and duly inspected the four remaining dolls.

"Very curious, sir—very unique, I think. Of course you see the idea, sir—the Four Seasons. Fifteenth-century Venetian, I should say. You can see the bit of brocade—old Venetian beyond a question. I wish I had half a dozen yards of it. Twenty guineas I'm asking for the set. I'm afraid I couldn't break the set. It's hardly fair to ask me, sir."

But eventually he yielded to the importunity of the customer and got five guineas for a second of his creations.

"Singular things, sir—Early Italian Church puppets beyond doubt. They used to dress them fantastically and stand them on the altar, I believe. You observe the symbolic character of the set, sir—the Trinity. Votive offerings and that, you know. Even in the present day you see such things at wayside shrines in Catholic countries. I'm afraid it would spoil the set to sell one out of the three, sir. You had better take the three now that you have the chance. Very unique, I call them, and only eighteen pounds for the three."

But the man had no use for the three, and after some haggling he got the one he wanted for £5, 10s.

"And then there were two," as the story of the ten little nigger boys has it.

"Church pieces, madam. Fourteenth-century Spanish—the embroidery is Spanish, I am sure. I wish I had a yard of it. Adam and Eve they are meant to represent," etc. etc.

It seemed as if no one could do with more than one of these "very unique" treasures; so he was forced to let the lady separate our first parents, paying five pounds for making the divorce decree absolute.

Before the end of the week he had sold a unique example of a Flemish doll —"One may see the like in some of Teniers' pictures. They treasure them up from generation to generation in the houses of the old nobility. It is very rarely that one gets into the market. You see they regard it as a matter of family honour never to sell one of them."

He sold it for six pounds, and took his wife to a theatre where, curiously enough, the diverting play of *La Poupée* was being performed. It is a diverting play, but not, I think, "absolutely unique."

It will be gathered from these instances of local business enterprise how amply the modern spirit of making the most of one's opportunities of "getting on" is represented among the commercial population of Burford. Its manufacturers may be divided into two classes: the makers and the fakers, and it is generally understood that the latter make the most money.

CHAPTER NINE—RED-TILED SOCIETY

I.   —THE ILLUSTRIOUS STRANGER

A̲LL THINGS ARE NOT WHAT THEY SEEM at Burford, as I have
ventured to suggest. But the majority of the inhabitants think that they are.
Probably at one time they were; but with the development of the spirit of
modern enterprise in the town a new complexion has been put upon various
features associated with the daily life of the place, so that one needs to go
beneath the surface of things in general in order to find out what they really
are.

It was literally the new complexion put upon a very ordinary commercial
undertaking that caused some of the most self-respecting of the inhabitants to
forget themselves upon one occasion a year or two ago. To be sure, they had
done nothing that should have caused even the most susceptible a qualm; but
they thought they had, and this impression was strengthened by the attitude of
a good many of their friends, so that the result was just as unpleasant to them
as if they had been guilty of some gross piece of foolishness.

The circumstances of this new complexion must be dealt with in detail in
order to be fully appreciated by people outside Burford.

When an announcement appeared in the local newspapers that the town
would shortly be visited by a distinguished Hindu, the Cachar of Darjeeling, a
considerable amount of excitement was caused in the best circles of Burford
Society—the best circles, it is scarcely necessary to say, are those that have
their centre somewhere in the new quarter, the bright red-brick villa quarter of
the town—and every one was inquiring what Mrs. Paston would do in the
matter. Mrs. Paston had obtained in many quarters an ample recognition of
her authority as *arbiter elegantarium*, and her lead in social matters was
regarded as inevitable even by those who could not conscientiously accept her
dicta as the last word on every point.

What will Mrs. Paston do when the Cachar of Darjeeling comes to
Burford? That was the question which people asked of one another over cups
of tea with occasional muffins; and the result of many conferences under
these or similar conditions was a resolution that a deputation of ladies
appointed themselves to wait on her, one at a time, to learn what she really
meant to do.

But it seemed that Mrs. Paston had not quite made up her mind on the
matter. The Cachar of Darjeeling is, of course, a prince—quite as much a
prince as the others one hears about—begums, sowdars, rajahs, jams, ranees,

gaekwars, khansamahs—all referred to by Mr. Kipling; and, of course, being a prince, he was, *ex officio*, eligible to be received even by the best people in Burford. To be sure, she had heard it said that—that—but for that matter there was as much wickedness at home, if people only took the trouble to look for it; and there was no need for people with daughters to put them forward in the presence of distinguished strangers, whether Indian princes or Austrian counts.

That was how Mrs. Paston took the various deputations of one into her confidence when they endeavoured to find out what she meant to do in regard to the coming visit of the distinguished Oriental, and they interpreted her mystic phrases as meaning that she meant to keep the Prince to herself. Within a few days the Cachar had come to be alluded to as "the Prince." In the English provinces practically every man of colour is accepted as a prince —it is a courtesy title, pretty much the same as the title of Madame which goes with a bonnet shop in the West End. Even the dusky person who accompanies the clergyman to the platform when a lecture is about to be given upon missionary work in the East, is referred to as "the Prince" that being the sanctioned English equivalent to his native title, which conveys nothing to the general public.

Yes, it seemed pretty clear that Mrs. Paston intended to keep the distinguished visitor to herself—that was why she made herself ambiguous when approached on the subject of his reception.

But there were other authorities besides Mrs. Pas-ton, and one of them was Mrs. Maxwell. She was the wife of a retired Indian Civil Servant, and the *quasi* Reception Committee showed some eagerness to learn what her attitude would be in regard to the coming Cachar of Darjeeling.

But Mrs. Maxwell said that her husband thought there had as usual been some misprint or mixing up of words in the paper, for he had never heard of the Cachar of Darjeeling; though there was a place named Cachar, and it was in Darjeeling, and very likely there was a prince or whatever they chose to call him in the neighbourhood.

This was not getting much farther on in the solution of the question that agitated the red-tiled group of Burford Society. It was pointed out by one sagacious lady that the fact of there being a place named Cachar in Darjeeling did not make it impossible that there should be a title of Cachar. They had not to go far from home for an example of this. Was there not a Lochiel in Scotland, and yet Lochiel was a place? Was there not a Magillicuddy in Ireland, and Magillicuddy was a mountain? It was pretty obvious that both Mrs. Maxwell and Mrs. Paston were temporising with the Committee; each was doing her best to put the others off the idea of leaving cards upon the

Cachar, hoping to take him under her own wing and keep him there.

That was the opinion of more than one of the inquirers, and a good deal of bitterness was occasioned by the reticence of the leaders. But no one seemed to know what was the object of the Princes visit to Burford, how long it was going to last, or with whom he meant to stay.

II.   —THE PRINCE'S PARADE

And then suddenly a stranger of dusky complexion and wearing flowing robes and a splendid turban set with precious stones appeared on foot in the High Street. He seemed greatly interested in the place, for he kept parading the leading thoroughfare and several of its byways practically the whole of the morning, so that he could scarcely escape the notice of all the residents who were in the town; no one failed to see him or to learn that he had taken lunch at Messrs. Caterham's new restaurant.

An hour later Mrs. Paston drove up to Caterham's. She inquired of one of the young ladies if the Cachar had rooms in the adjoining hotel, and learned that he was resting in the private room at the back of the restaurant.

She at once sent in her card.

Hardly had she done so when Mrs. Lake entered and greeted her—Mrs. Lake was another of the red-tiled residents—saying—"I hear that the Prince is here. I suppose you have sent your card to him—I am sending mine. It is our duty, I think, to show some civility to such a visitor. My brother, you know, is intimately associated with India—Woods and Forests, you know."

She passed her card to the young lady, and smiled at Mrs. Paston in a way that was meant to assure her that she was mistaken if she fancied that she was to have the Prince all to herself.

"I am sure that the Prince will be delighted to hear that your brother is in —— What did you say he was in?" asked Mrs. Paston sweetly.

"Woods and Forests—the most important Department in all India," said the other. "My brother would never forgive me if I allowed the Prince to come here without showing him some civility."

They were going together to the door when they found themselves face to face with Mrs. Markham and her daughter, both dressed as if for a garden party, and close behind them came Major Sowerby of the Territorials and his son, for whom he had been unsuccessfully trying to get a billet for the previous two years.

"Glad to see you here, Mrs. Paston," cried the Major heartily. "Yes, I maintain that it is our duty to welcome—to stretch out a right hand of greeting to the natives of our great Dependency—one Empire—one Flag—hands across the sea—that's what I have always advocated. I am wondering if he couldn't do something for my Teddy here. I believe these rajahs and memsahibs and cachars have got no end of money—rupees—the old Pagoda tree and that. Teddy can turn his hand to anything."

The expression of his excellent patriotic sentiments was interrupted by the arrival of nearly all the members of the Committee of inquiry, and a card-case was in the hand of every one of them, and other ladies of the élite were hurrying down the street, plainly making the restaurant their objective. Within a quarter of an hour a whole salver of cards had been taken charge of by the young lady, some of them bearing a few pencilled words: "Hoping to be honoured by a visit," "At home every day this week at 4," "Trusting to obtain permission to receive H.H. the Cachar," and the like. Mrs. Lake had written on hers, "Sister of Mr. George Barnes, Woods and Forests Dept.," and Major Sowerby had put in parenthesis under his son's name, "Ellison prizeman at Routilla College, Eastbourne."

The next day the Prince appeared once again promenading the High Street. He was a man of fine presence, of a rich ruddy brown complexion and a black beard and moustache, and his turban was a sight! It contained a central diamond little inferior in size to the Koh-i-noor, and on each side of it was a pigeon's egg ruby—a lady who saw it called it a pigeon's blood ruby lest there should be any mistake: a casual glance of some one who did not know all about these great jewels might convey the impression that it was only a bantam's blood ruby, which was quite an inferior stone. He had an air of distinction which caused him to be greatly admired, and yet he was so devoid of any foolish pride that he did not hesitate to chat quite pleasantly to one of the young ladies in Caterham's. (Mrs! Paston, hearing this, expressed the hope that the young lady would be very careful. But Major Sowerby, when it reached his ears, said he hoped the Prince would be careful. Mrs. Markham said nothing, but glanced hopefully at her daughter.)

MRS MARKHAM'S DAUGHTER

All the ladies remained under their rosy tiles that afternoon, and all the maids were supplied with the whitest of caps and aprons. Tea was delayed in every house for three-quarters of an hour: there was no knowing what might happen. But nothing happened. The Cachar of Darjeeling was clearly feeling the embarrassment of having to respond to a welcome offered in such plurality; though Mrs. Paston thought that surely one of the young ladies in Caterham's would have told him to whom he should give precedence in making his calls. Every other lady was of the same opinion.

Mrs. Paston thought it but right that she should give the Prince some encouragement, so she wrote a little note to him inviting his confidence as to his plans, and hoping that he might be able to lunch with her the next day, when she would have great pleasure in driving him to Lady Collingby's annual Flower Show. Four other ladies addressed notes to him expressing precisely the same sentiments, and all set out to deliver them at Caterham's with their own hands, to save the delay of a post.

They entered Caterham's almost simultaneously, without noticing that the hoarding which had been built about the next door premises while a plate-glass front of noble design was being set in its place had been removed. And when they inquired for the Cachar, the young lady said—"He is in the new shop—you go through the arch on the left."

There was a Norman arch of lath and plaster enriched by insets of highly decorated Lincrusta—the paper-hangmen had just left it—in the partition wall; through it the ladies went and found themselves in a spacious shop with a profusion of cheap specimens of Oriental china on lacquer brackets about the walls, and an all-pervading smell of freshly roasted coffee. It was clearly the newly acquired premises of the enterprising Messrs. Caterham, which they meant to run as a shop for the sale of Indian tea and West Indian coffee —the "Old Flag" was their trade-mark—and a brisk sale of half-pound and quarter-pound packets was going on at the counter.

So much the ladies who had just entered could see; but a moment after they had taken their first illuminating glance round the place they stood with their eyes fixed upon one of the most prominent objects of the place—the bustling figure of the Cachar of Darjeeling in native dress, turban and jewels and all, tying up parcels of tea behind the counter, and testing the coins which the crowd of customers tendered in payment before pulling the bell-ringing drawer of the cash register!

The enterprise of Messrs. Caterham had suggested to them the advertising attraction in the form of a full-robed Oriental at the head of their new tea department. They had promoted one of their old hands—he came from the East End of London—to the post, and having "made up" under the guidance of one of Messrs. Nathan's most highly qualified assistants, Messrs. Caterham were perhaps not going too far when they asserted in their advertisements that the tea trade of Burford would assume an entirely new complexion.

The ladies gazed in horrible fascination upon the impostor—at the moment they were unable to differentiate between an advertisement and an impostor—for nearly a whole minute, and then they turned and walked slowly away without exchanging a word.

Mrs. Paston left Burford the next day, having been ordered by her medical adviser to Buxton. But Major Sowerby picked out his most serviceable Malacca cane, and was heard to declare, while trying its balance in downward strokes from left to right, that he had only to come across that scoundrel who called himself by the honourable title of a loyal Indian potentate in order to teach him a lesson that he would remember so long as he had breath in his body.

101

The general impression that prevailed throughout Burford, however, so soon as the story of the exclusive ladies and their Indian prince was in full circulation—and it did not take long to pass round the town—was that the incident should teach a lesson to a good many people who take it upon them to lead the red-tiled society of the new town.

But whether they learn any lesson or not, there seems to be a consensus of opinion that the sooner the name of the High Street is changed to Prince's Parade the better it will be for the town, Messrs. Caterham, and, incidentally, Mr. Isaac Moss, professionally known as the Cachar of Darjeeling. (As a matter of fact, there are already several people not belonging to the governing classes who, ever since the episode just recorded, have invariably alluded to the lower part of the High Street—that part which has been annexed by Messrs. Caterham—as the Prince's Parade.)

CHAPTER TEN—LESSER ENGLISH COUNTRY TOWNS

I. —STARKIE AND THE STATES

I REMEMBER WITH WHAT ADROITNESS several years ago a distinguished dramatist explained to a pressing interviewer what was his intention in writing a certain play of his which was being widely discussed in many directions. It was merely to show how dangerous it was for any man to wander off the beaten track, he said: "A man must keep in line with his fellow-men if he hopes to avoid disaster"—and so forth. The explanation was no doubt accounted quite satisfactory by such persons as had been perturbed on the matter to which it referred.

It certainly would have been accepted with every token of assent by the majority of the inhabitants of the lesser English country towns. They regard as highly dangerous to the community the least departure from the primrose path of the commonplace. They have a hymn which goes—

> "We are travelling home to God
>
> In the way our fathers trod,
>
> They are happy now, and we
>
> Soon their happiness shall see."

"THE WAY OUR FATHERS TROD"

🖺

The stanza embodies their highest aspirations; and really, when one comes to consider the whole matter, one could hardly formulate a more satisfactory walk of life; only it is a walk, not a race, and some people (outside a country town) look to go through life at a faster pace. "In the way our fathers trod"— that is the sound motto of the country town, and the man who tries to get out of the old ruts is looked upon with suspicion by the sensible people to whom he may allude as old rutters or even old rotters.

A middle-aged inhabitant of a town nearly twice as large as our Mallingham was greatly impressed with this truth by an incident which had just come under his notice when I had occasion to call upon him some time ago. He told me that he had been visited by a former townsman of his, but one whom he had not seen for more than fifteen years.

"No, you wouldn't remember Joseph Starkie, old Sol Starkie's son," he said to me in the course of his narrative. "It was before you came to county. Queer restless chap was Joe always."

"Is he any relation to the Starkie who invented the magnetic lathe that is used everywhere in the States?" I inquired.

"I shouldn't wonder," he replied, as if making a sad admission. "Yes, I believe he said something about it when he was with me. He was just that sort of chap—so restless and dissatisfied always—wanting to do things differently from how they had always been done. His father was a most respectable man, however, in the hardware line, and Joe was too much for him: he packed him off to an uncle in the States, and there he has been ever since, he told me. "Sad—very sad! His father had quite a nice little business here, and if Joe had only settled down reasonably he might have succeeded to it and done well."

"It strikes me that he has done pretty well elsewhere," said I. "His name is well known in every machine shop in the States."

"Is that so? Well, maybe so; but that's not like having a comfortable place at home. Why, he might even have had a seat at the Town Council or the Water Board in time. When he came in here to-day I knew him at once; but I wasn't too eager with him until I saw from his way that he hadn't come to borrow money, as I feared at first. He wanted to inquire about some of his old associates, and he knew that I could tell him. 'Where's Johnnie Vance?' he asked. 'I looked in at his old office just now and no one seemed disposed to tell me.' I shook my head and pointed up the road. He saw what I meant. 'Jail?' he whispered. 'Jail? What was the trouble?' 'Embezzlement,' I told him. 'Well, well, who would have thought it?' he said. 'And maybe you can tell me if Willie Rossiter is still in his old crib,' he asked. I shook my head. 'Don't tell me that he's in jail too,' he cried. 'No, no—at least, not exactly. I want to be fair to every one. It's not jail, only the asylum.' 'What!' he said. 'Willie Rossiter—the asylum? How did it come about—an accident?' It went against my grain to tell him that it was drink, but he pressed me and I had to do it; and then he went on to talk about the old town for some time, but I could see that he had another friend to ask about. He pretended to be at the point of going and then suddenly to remember that there was somebody else. Jimmy Gray—it was Jimmy Gray. 'By the bye,' he said, 'I wonder if old Jimmy Gray is still knocking about.' I smiled. 'No, he's not doing much knocking about just now,' I told him. 'Not dead?' he asked. 'Oh no,' said I; 'only he has just taken rooms in the Bridgend Hotel.' 'What! the workhouse?' he cried. 'The workhouse indeed,' said I. 'And nobody would have known anything about it if he hadn't made a fool of himself writing to the Board of Guardians complaining that he had been kept waiting for a quarter of an hour when he had applied for admission.' That was the last of his inquiries after his old friends. But they had all been restless chaps like himself—not settling down to anything properly. Still, he didn't ask me to lend him any money, and that was something."

I could scarcely fail to see that this exemplary citizen felt keenly the value of the dramatist's suggestion, that it is very dangerous for a man to fall out of line with the rest of the community. Social laws exist for the community, not for the individual. At the same time, I was not so firmly convinced as my friend seemed to be that Mr. Starkie's career could be pointed to as a notable instance of the peril of marching out of the way our fathers trod. He had declined to yield to the influences of the magnet that "hung in the hardware shop" of his father, and had so forsaken the two hundred a year and the obscurity of his native town for the million dollars which he had earned by his inventions in Pennsylvania, to say nothing of the fame which accrues to an inventor who knows how to put his inventions on the market; so that there might really be some people ready to assert that Joe Starkie's restlessness suggested that a divergence from the scheme of the Red-man on the warpath, who is careful to step into the footprints of the man who goes before him, may now and again be advisable. I did not say so to my exemplary citizen, however; for the fame of Joe Starkie had not yet reached the place of his nativity, and the exemplary citizen might have asked me what about Joe Starkie's old friends who were now sojourning in various public institutions, and he would not have been satisfied with my replying to the effect that they had stayed at home, and were suffering for it.

II. —OUR FATHERS' FOOTSTEPS

In the way our fathers trod"—that seems to be the proud boast of the English country towns, and I am not sure that it is not a worthy one, though its application to certain cases is certainly humorous. I remember revisiting a town where I had once lived, and getting into conversation with an elderly and well-to-do inhabitant. I mentioned having met in London a surgeon who had been born in and lived in the town. He certainly enjoyed the largest practice in London, and, in addition to the K.C.B., bore as many continental orders as permitted of his wearing (which he did) a very dingy dress-coat without its dinginess being perceptible. His reputation had, however, eluded the cognizance of his native town.

"What a fool he was to go off to London, when he might have done so well here," was the comment of the elderly citizen upon my proud boast that I had met Sir William in London. "If he had only held on here he might by this time have got the best dispensary in the town."

I did not doubt it.

He took the same view in regard to the career of another eminent townsman, who, I mentioned, had just been made an F.R.S.

"If he had been wise and carried on his father's business here he might have been a J.P. by now," was his solemn comment.

I thought it better to refrain from any further remarks, lest I should be made to feel more acutely than I did all that I had forfeited by my premature departure from a town that offered such prizes for obscurity.

There are still a large number of country towns in England where the feeling still remains that any departure from their precincts is, if not absolutely fatal, at any rate risky. I have met people in more than one town who looked on a man's going to America as equivalent to absconding. I suppose most of these places have some foundation of their own for the tradition. It is quite plausible that, seventy or eighty or even a hundred years ago, some wild young men may have found a voyage to America to offer them a satisfactory alternative to an appearance behind the spikes of the dock of the County Court-House, and America got a bad name in consequence, being looked on as a continent peopled by men who had gone wrong at home. However this may be, I must confess that I was startled, when I first came to Thurswell and mentioned that I heard that a young man who had played a good deal of lawn-tennis during the summer was going to the States, by the inquiry—

"Why, what has he been doing anyway?"

It did not come from one of the rustic population, but from a tradesman in quite a good way of business—a considerable proportion of it in canned provisions into the bargain.

I believe that when Dr. Watson, the author of *Beside the Bonnie Brier Bush*, went on his first lecturing tour to America, the financial results of which were so satisfactory, an impression prevailed in certain directions that the act was unworthy of a clergyman of the Presbyterian Church, and he was made the object of a severe attack in some quarters.

One can easily appreciate the attitude of people who have lived all their lives in an English country town in regard to the restless members of a family. One has only to walk through a churchyard and read the names on the tombs to understand how deeply rooted in the soil are the people. So far as Thurswell and Mallingham are concerned, a stroll through one of the churchyards is almost equivalent to studying a directory. The same names as are cut upon the tombs—some of them going back a hundred and fifty years—are to be seen over the shop windows to-day and on the dairy carts and the farm carts. In some cases the name of a yeoman ancestor reappears in a Grand Jury list, indicating a material advance in the social scale. The migration that has been going on in our county for the past two hundred years seems to be interparochial. Individuals moved from village to village and from village to town. It is only within the past twenty-five or thirty years that the ablest and the best have occasionally braved public opinion and set sail for a colony.

Even families that have "got on" seem to love to cling to the county which saw the very small beginnings of their ancestors. Why should they not? Love of one's county is only a subdivision of the grand virtue of love of one's country. It was only when a certain aged doctor, who had the family history of our neighbourhood at his fingers' ends for over sixty years, published a volume of interesting reminiscences, in the course of which he took occasion to refer to the very humble beginnings of some families that considered themselves very "swagger," that we learned how tenaciously they had clung to their county. Even the slow-moving Mallingham is not without its romances of "getting on." One of the most intrepid motorists in the borough is remembered by several middle-aged burgesses as the wearer of the green baize apron and the wielder of the broom of the caretaker and window-cleaner of a solicitor's office; and from what I know of him I am inclined to believe that that was the best kept office in the town when he had charge of it.

CHAPTER ELEVEN—THE CATHEDRAL TOWN

I.—IN THE SHADOW OF THE MINSTER

BROADMINSTER IS ONE OF THE LESSER cathedral towns of England. There is nothing remarkable about the Minster except its antiquity. It does not convey the idea of vastness as do some of these venerable buildings. One would never imagine oneself in the midst of a petrified forest on passing through the porch. The carving about the pillars does not suggest lacework in stone, though it is admirable in its way, and the screen shows signs of having been "restored" in the days when restoration meant spoliation. The coloured glass of the windows is not especially good, but the oldest is undoubtedly the best. The modern memorial windows were apparently estimated for and the specification of the lowest-priced competitor accepted; but, really, the Chapter should have prevented the perpetration of such a blunder as that of the artist who, in his representation of the entrance to the sacred tomb, with the sleeping Roman guards on each side, put a crescent moon in the very blue sky! But for that matter, when I pointed out the mistake to one of the higher canons, he did not perceive for some time that the Paschal moon was bound to be within a few days of the full.

The old Minster is, however, worthy of every respect, if it does not quite inspire such feelings of reverence and awe as does Westminster Abbey or Canterbury or Durham or Santa Croce at Florence. One feels that it is the sort of building one can trust. It is solid throughout, and that is something. I remember years ago, when I was lecturing a long-suffering group on the marvels of Milan, calling attention to the wonderful scheme of lighting by which the High Altar was made the centre of illumination, I observed some shadows of the stone spandrels on the roof for which I could not account. There the light spines and ridges flowed upward to meet at the apex, and there the shadows slept, increasing the effect amazingly. Only after some patient investigation did I find that the groins were painted on the woodwork to imitate the stone where the stonework ended!

If there is nothing to wonder at in the interior of Broadminster, there is at least something to trust. It is sound throughout.

But why, oh! why, should that old woman be allowed to stand just outside the porch with a basket of nuts on her arm, offering them for sale to all visitors?

A stranger within our gates was puzzled by this apparition at the door of the church. He had just come from London, and he had been taken to the Zoo. He looked for some reason for the nuts at Broadminster—reason and consistency.

If nuts, why not buns, he wished me to explain to him.

I felt incapable of clearing away this mystery. I could not tell him, under the shadow of the sacred building, the legend that I invented to account for the nuts, but I told him in full when we got away from that influence of veracity: it had to do with a crusader who, forsaken by his comrades in the Lebanon, was forced to sustain himself with nuts, and vowed that if ever he should get back to England he would endow a Minster and decree that nuts should be offered at the porch between prime and angelus every day for a thousand years. He kept his vow, hence——

That was eight hundred and eighty-two years ago, so that only one hundred and twenty of the vow had yet to run, and then——

He was barely satisfied with this explanation. I could scarcely blame him: it did not satisfy myself.

There are some people who think that the best part of St. Ursula—the Minster is dedicated to St. Ursula—is the Close. The Deanery, and the residences of the canons, major and minor, and all the officials of the Cathedral, lay as well as clerical, stand on two sides of a square, with the old building in the centre. Green meadows with a glimpse of green hills beyond are on the other sides of the square, and just behind the houses of the Close flows the Avonbeck, a narrow winding river in which trout may be caught by the dozen by the least skilful fisherman.

The beautiful gardens of the Close slope down to the banks of the river.

I was told a pathetic story by the wife of one of the dignitaries respecting a young man who had never any especial leaning for the Church as a career, but who made up his mind, when he saw this Close and walked through the gardens and fished in the Avonbeck, that the Church was the only possible profession for him. He went through the usual course, was ordained, and appointed to a parish in a slum in the Midlands, where he has remained ever since—and that was twenty-five years ago.

Equally pathetic, however, to some people may be the case of the clergyman who practically started life as one of the lesser dignitaries of the Cathedral and has remained there ever since—and that was thirty-five years ago. It was said that he was once a good preacher, and even now he seldom falls more than a couple of tones in going from the Responses to the Prayers. He began with high ideas regarding Greek texts, but now he devotes himself to Canadian trout. He has great hopes, he told me, for the future of Canadian trout.

II.   —THE NEW PALACE

The Palace of the Bishop of Broadminster is not, of course, among the buildings of the Close. It stands in its own grounds about two miles away, and it bears tokens of having been built within the last quarter of a century. It did not start life as a palace, but as the country house of a business man in a bustling town. The story of how it became the Palace is a curious one.

The original Palace was a big square barrack of a place, costing a great deal to keep up and giving no adequate return for its upkeep. It was a survival of the days when a bishop was expected to maintain a retinue of servants and never to go out for a quiet drive unless four horses were harnessed to the coach. The stables were built to accommodate twenty-two horses: it seemed to be understood that no self-respecting bishop could do with less, so long-lived are the Church traditions of the Middle Ages; and the servant retinue was expected to be maintained in the same proportion. The consequence was that the revenues of the diocese were quite insufficient to do more than keep up the place; they left nothing over for the poor Bishop himself, who could do very well with a 15 h.p. motor and a garage 25' x 15', a single chauffeur, and a gardener, instead of six horses, a coachman, an under-coachman, four grooms, and nine gardeners.

Every now and again the question of the requirements of the Palace as opposed to the requirements of the Bishop was cropping up, and certain newspapers published letters from ignorant and irresponsible correspondents in which the phrases "bloated revenues," "princely prelates," "modern Wolseys," and the like recurred, particular emphasis being laid upon the fact that his lordship kept no fewer than eleven gardeners—a very moderate exaggeration—for his own personal gratification as a horticulturist. And all this was very harassing for the poor Bishop.

Now in the years when the upkeep of both the Bishop and the Palace was becoming a serious problem, there was living in a bustling manufacturing town a hundred miles from Broadminster a quiet little business man named Robinson. He had begun life in a rather small way; but before he was forty, having no expensive tastes and being engaged in a lucrative business, he had made a fortune—not, of course, such a fortune as may be made in the United States in these days, but still a fortune for an English provincial town. It so happened that he lodged with two maiden sisters slightly older than himself, and when he was about fifty he asked the elder to marry him. She agreed, and married they were.

After living a year or two in the house in which he had lodged they started a one-horse brougham, and a little later Mrs. Robinson had a fancy to live in the country; and as her husband invariably thought as she did on every subject, he at once set about building a house that would always be worth (his architect assured him) the money he spent upon it. Mrs. Robinson being a pious woman and liking the Cathedral service, the site of the house should be, they determined, within easy reach of Broadminster.

It was an admirable house when it was finished, and the three-acre garden could easily be managed by one man and a boy. This was in the days when a financial episode, known as the brewery boom, was beginning to be felt throughout the country, and it was known that Mr. Robinson had made as much in a week out of brewery shares as paid for the house he had built and the gardens that had been laid out for him by a competent landscape architect. And on the first morning that he breakfasted in their new home he presented his wife with the title-deeds of the whole, and made over the furniture to her as well.

For five years they lived there in great happiness, and it was known that they were devoted to each other; but before they entered on their sixth year Mrs. Robinson died, and her husband found that she had made a will leaving the house and grounds and furniture to the Church authorities—whoever they were—for the use of the existing Bishop of Broadminster and his successors for ever.

It appeared that Mrs. Robinson had become aware of the Palace difficulty, and made up her mind that she should do her best to solve the question of providing a reasonable residence for the Bishop in place of that insatiable monstrous barrack which he had been compelled to occupy, and upon which he was forced to spend every penny of his income.

Although the will rather startled Mr. Robinson—for his wife had not confided in him that it was her intention to provide for the Bishop and his successors—he had no fault to find with it. He confessed to a friend that his dear wife had solved a question that might have perplexed himself; for he had no relative to whom he might reasonably be expected to leave the place.

But before many days had passed he received a message from the ecclesiastical solicitors begging him to have the goodness to let them know at his convenience when it would suit him to give their clients possession of the house: and then he was really startled. A visit to his own solicitor made him aware of the fact that no provision had been made in his wife's will for allowing him to continue residing in the house or using the furniture therein— that he was, in fact, a trespasser in the house that he had built for himself!

A little thought, however, convinced him that as soon as the facts of the case became known to the Church authorities there would be no trouble in obtaining their consent to his remaining on in the house; but it soon appeared that he had been rather too sanguine on this point. It was explained to him that the authorities were unfortunately left without any option in the matter, and possession of the place must be given to them within three months, rent for this period to be paid by him at a rate that might be agreed between his solicitor and themselves. They were ecclesiastically courteous, but legally firm, and so Mr. Robinson had to leave the house on which he had spent many hours of loving and intelligent thought the gardens to which he had given particular attention while they were being laid out, and the furniture which he had selected piece by piece from the best makers.

He was allowed to take away his own clothes, however, and he began to feel that this was a concession.

He went to Lausanne and died there a few years later, leaving about a hundred thousand pounds to various charities, but none of them having any connection with Broadminster.

Before the end of the year in which the property was acquired by the Church it became the Palace, Broadminster: previously it had been called Leighside Hall.

And from that day it is understood that the Bishop has been saving money to make up for the years which the early locust abode of his had eaten.

III.   —ANTE-MORTEM GENEROSITY

Curiously enough, there stands within view of the new Palace another house with a history attached to it which may strike some people as illustrating, with a humour that is still more grim, the inconvenience resulting from ante-mortem generosity on a large scale: post-mortem generosity may occasionally be risky, but its display on even the most lavish scale has never been known to cause any personal inconvenience to the one who indulges in it.

The house is an interesting old Jacobean one, standing on the side of a mound within a loop of the river.

It has consequently a series of terrace gardens which are quite delightful at all seasons. For years it was occupied by a Captain Hesketh and his wife, the latter having inherited it with a handsome fortune from her mother, who was the heiress of a family of considerable importance in the county. At her husband's death Mrs. Hesketh continued to live alone in the old house with a niece—for she had no children of her own—and in course of time the girl fell in love with a man who seemed in every way the right sort of person for her to marry, only for the fact of his having a very limited income. The girl's aunt, however, having nothing to live for except the witnessing of the happiness of the young couple, was generous enough to make over to them all her property, retaining only a sufficient sum to enable her to live in comfort for the remainder of her life.

At this time she was sixty-three years of age, and her wants were very simple. It is said that the annuity which she purchased amounted to no more than three hundred pounds a year. Twelve years later, however, the lawyer whom she had entrusted to carry out this portion of the transaction for her died, and an examination of his affairs revealed the fact that, instead of spending the money which she had handed to him in the purchase of an annuity guaranteed by an Insurance Company of good reputation, he had treated it as his own, and had merely paid her a quarterly allowance. He died a bankrupt, owing thousands of pounds to clients whose money he had appropriated; so that at the age of seventy-five the unfortunate lady found herself penniless.

Her position was annoying, she told the man from whom I had the story, but she did not feel it to be serious. Of course, she had only to explain matters to her niece and her niece's husband and they would take care that she should not suffer through the swindling agent. She hastened to have an interview with them on the subject, and was actually smiling as she told them what had happened. She was not smiling, however, when the interview terminated; for she found herself treated by them as a begging stranger. They gave her a sound scolding for her unbusinesslike credulity: the idea of entrusting her money to such a man without taking the trouble to find out how he had invested it! The thing was absurd—grossly absurd, and they thought that she deserved to suffer for her culpable carelessness!

Of course, though surprised and hurt at this want of sympathy, the old lady readily admitted that she had been very careless; but the man had been her lawyer and her husband's lawyer for over thirty years, and she had implicit confidence in him, she said. After all, she reminded her relations that she was an old woman, and that in all probability she would not be a burden to them for more than a few years.

This plea did not seem to soften them in any way; at any rate, it did not prevent her niece from expressing the opinion that it was most inconsiderate on her part to expect that she and her husband should accept the responsibility of keeping her for the rest of her life. They had two children to educate, she explained, and it was going too far to expect that they should be made to suffer because of her stupidity.

The poor old lady felt herself turned out of her old house—the house in which she might still have been living if she had not been so foolishly generous.

The next day, however, she received a letter from her niece's husband informing her that, after due consideration of the matter, he and his wife had come to the conclusion that, although she had no claim whatsoever upon them, they might be able to allow her a pound a week for life. He trusted that she had saved enough during the previous twelve years to allow of her living comfortably—many women, he reminded her, were compelled to live on much less. The final sentence in his letter was equivalent to an exhortation to her to thank Heaven for having given her a niece of so generous a disposition.

The story reached the ears of a lady who had been her friend for many years, and she insisted on her rejecting the alms of her niece, offering her a home with herself, and expressing her happiness to receive her under her roof. The old lady accepted her friend's invitation; but at the same time she made application to be admitted as an inmate to a certain almshouse which had been founded and endowed by one of her own ancestors. This step, however, she took in secret, and at least a year would have to elapse before she could hope for admission to the charity.

It so happened, however, that her generous friend had a son who had obtained some eminence at the Bar, and it seemed that the grim humour of the whole story appealed to him very strongly. But on thinking over the matter he perceived that this element in the story was not so finished as he thought it should be, if properly worked out by an ironic fate. He considered himself to be something of a critic in such matters, and it was possibly his artistic instinct that prompted him to make a move with a view to remedy the deficiency that he perceived in the story. He had acquired a pretty fair knowledge of men and their characteristics, and it occurred to him that a solicitor who gave up so much of his attention to the movements of stocks and shares as did this dishonest one who was the cause of the old lady's disaster, might possibly have been guilty of some neglect in respect of the deeds of gift conveying her property to her niece, and he turned his attention in this direction. He knew exactly what legal machinery to put in motion for the purpose of his inquiry, and the result he considered highly satisfactory; but it is doubtful if the ungrateful niece of the poor lady for whom the solicitor he had engaged was acting was of the same opinion when she received notice that a motion was about to be made before His Majesty's judges to set aside the deed of gift made twelve years earlier on account of a vital flaw in the document itself.

The ungrateful niece and her husband consulted their solicitor when they received their shock. He laughed reassuringly at first.

"Sounds very like a bit of bluff," said he. "What does it mean? Why should your aunt want to get into her hands again the property that she made over to you?"

The man told him that the lady had been the victim of a rascally solicitor, and so was left without a penny.

"And now she seems to have got into the hands of another of the same stamp, only worse," said the lawyer. "I don't think you need be uneasy. I'll get a copy of the original deed and get counsel's opinion about it. Trent will be the man. I'll send it to Trent. He is the leading man for that sort of thing. If there's any flaw in it he'll be able to lay his finger on it."

The two clients looked at each other with something like dismay on their faces.

"My aunt has been living for the past three months with a Mrs. Trent, I have heard," said the lady.

The lawyer opened his eyes unusually wide and screwed up his mouth into the form of a puckered O.

"She is his mother," he said after a pause. "But why—why should he bother about such a piece of business as this? Why should he be interested in upsetting the deed when it was obviously the intention of your aunt to present you with the property? You have not quarrelled with her, have you?"

"Oh no, there was no quarrel. She came to us with her story, of course, and we at once offered to do something for her," replied the niece.

"Of course. That was the sensible thing to do. But this only makes the matter seem more mysterious. She accepted your offer, I suppose, and why, then, she should——"

"She didn't accept it."

"What! Did she make a demand on you to return the whole property?"

"Never. But she suggested that we should make good the three hundred a year of her annuity."

"But isn't that what you say you promised her?"

"We told her we couldn't afford that; but we offered her fifty-two pounds a year."

"A pound a week—one pound a week? Oh, my dear lady! A pound a week! Surely you are joking."

"We thought that she must surely have saved a good deal during the twelve years."

"Three hundred a year, when you deduct the in-come tax, doesn't leave a gentlewoman much margin for saving."

The man of the law shook his head and assumed a very serious look.

"Of course, I can't say anything at this moment as to the sort of case they have against you; but I do not feel justified in concealing from you my impression that if it is as we suppose, and Mr. Trent has pronounced against the deed, the Court will take his view of it. Trent is not the man to try on any sharp practice. And my advice to you is to make any sacrifice to prevent the case from going before the Court. Trent, if he is moving in the matter, must feel the ground pretty firm under his feet. What a pity it was that you did not suggest three hundred a year to the lady instead of—oh, that was undoubtedly a mistake—a pound a week. Well, we can only do our best in the circumstances. Who are the solicitors that sent you the letter?"

The lady gave him the name of the firm, and in due course he communicated with them. An examination of the doubtful document removed the possibility of his retaining any doubt as to its being invalid, and his clients were assured that they could not contend the case there was against them.

119

After this, I suppose, there was a scene that could only have justice done to its varied features by the pen of a gifted novelist. I can see the weeping niece on her knees in front of the old lady who had been her benefactrix, but whom she had repaid with gross ingratitude. Her children would possibly be kneeling by her side—they certainly would on the lyric stage or in the last chapter of the novel. No doubt the aunt would be greatly affected, though properly reproachful. But I doubt if the gallery of the theatre or the readers of the novelette would be quite satisfied with the conclusion of the story; for the generous aunt allowed her original gift to stand, only stipulating for her three hundred a year out of the estate.

Whatever humour one may perceive in these stories is certainly of that unusual type which one might expect to find associated with a cathedral town. It is the humour of an Old Testament parable—hard, and with a lesson attached to it.

Not precisely of the same nature was the definition of the duties of the verger suggested by a promising youth, whom I had instructions to lead round the Minster by his relations: they intended him to become an architect, and thought that he should become acquainted with the design of all the cathedrals to begin with. At first he supposed that the dignified gentleman wearing the black gown and carrying a mysterious emblem of authority was an archbishop, and I fear I failed to place him in possession of the facts respecting the duties of the verger, for he nodded, saying—"Ah yes, I understand—a sort of dignified chuck-er-out."

It is not on record that there was attached to any great ecclesiastical institution a dignitary who discharged the duties of a calcitrator. And, so far as Broadminster is concerned, one may say that, whatever brawls disturb the peace of other churches upon occasions, tranquillity reigns within these grey walls and harmony among the spirits of its fortunate aisles.

IV.   —THE BLACK SHEEP

Only the merest echo of a rumour of years ago regarding a parson who managed to creep into the Chapter when he should have been excluded survives to-day. And even this attenuated scandal would have faded away long ago if some people had not kept it alive by a story which owes its point to the use made of the shady parson's name by an old reprobate who desired to score off a worthy clergyman. The worthy clergyman had come to pay a serious parochial visit of remonstrance to the old reprobate, and had made up his mind, in antique slang, to "let him have it hot." He had tried the velvet glove of the kindly counsellor several times with the same man, and now he determined to see what the mailed fist would do. Chronic intoxication was the old reprobate's besetting sin, and that was—with more frequent intervals of repentance—the particular failing of that parson who had been a thorn in the flesh to the Cathedral Chapter. It was, however, the vice of which the visiting clergyman was most intolerant; so he launched out in fitting terms against the old reprobate, demonstrating to him how disgraceful, how senseless a thing it was to be a sot.

THE OLD REPROBATE

The man listened to him until the first pause came, and then he sighed, saying—"Truer words were never spoken, sir, and no one knows that better than yourself, Mr. Weston."

Now Weston was the name of the frail parson, who had been dead for several years, and to hear himself so addressed was very nettling to the teetotal clergyman.

"My name is not Weston," he said sharply. "You know that I am Mr. Walters."

"I ask your pardon, sir," said the man. "But I hold with all you say, and no one has ever said the same better than yourself, Mr. Weston."

"Don't call me Weston," cried the clergyman. "The fact that you are muddled on a simple matter like this shows clearly to what condition you have sunk."

"I don't doubt it, sir," acquiesced the man sadly. "It's not a condition for any human to be, though mayhap it's worse when it overtakes a passon, as I'm sure you'll hold with me, Mr. Weston."

"I was informed that you had been sober for some days," said the clergyman. "But I now begin to fear that you are far from being anything like sober. Have you had anything to drink to-day?"

"Not a drop—not a drop, I'm sorry to confess to you, Mr. Weston."

The good parson sprang to his feet.

"You are a wretched man!" he cried. "You are clearly so bemuddled with that poison that you are incapable of recognising who is speaking to you."

"Nay, nay, sir; I'm not so far gone as that. I'm never so far gone but that I can know when a passon's a-speaking to me, Mr. Weston. I s'pose 'tis summit in their manner o' speech, Mr. Weston."

The tortured clergyman caught up his hat and rushed from the cottage.

Few people would have given the old reprobate credit for striking upon so subtle a scheme of retaliation upon the clergyman who was a model of rectitude, had not the clergyman himself been indiscreet enough to complain, as he did with great bitterness, that the horrid old man was so fuddled with drink as to be incapable of differentiating between a cleric who had never been in the shadow of a cloud and one who had never been otherwise than shady, and who, moreover, had been among the shades for several years.

There were, however, some people who had had experience of the readiness of resources of the old reprobate, and who knew how he had aimed at getting even with his upright visitor. And so the story spread, and was the means of keeping green, if one may be allowed the metaphor, the unsavoury memory of the thorn in the flesh of the Chapter.

But if the wicked old man only simulated for his own base purposes a mistake as to the identity of Mr. Walters, there was certainly no such evil intention on the part of a young woman who, when on a visit to a relation living in Broadminster, was invited to a dinner party and was taken in by a fine-looking man of military appearance whose name was pronounced by their hostess as Colonel Trelawney. The lady rather prided herself on being equal to converse with men of any profession, and she at once started with her partner at the table on a military topic, and continued to ply him with questions of a more or less technical sort, on most of which he professed an ignorance surprising in one who had attained to the rank of a commanding officer. She almost became cross with the completeness of her failure to draw him out; but just as the cheese straws were going round she asked him in desperation if there was any branch of the Service in which he was interested.

"Well," he said, "of course I am interested in every part of it, but just now I have been studying all the authorities on the order of the Creeds, and I must confess that I find them enthralling."

She was puzzled.

"Are you in the Sappers?" she asked after a long pause. She had heard that some of the Sappers had peculiarities.

"The Sappers?" he repeated. "The Sappers? I'm afraid I don't quite understand your question. How could I——"

"Are you not Colonel Trelawney?" she cried.

"I am Canon Trelawney," he replied. "What! Is it possible that you fancied —oh, it must be so. That is why you have been talking on military topics all this time. Colonel! Oh, this is really amusing! Colonel!"

"I thought that our hostess had said 'Colonel,'" she murmured. "You must have fancied that I was mad."

"It was largely my own fault," said he. "I am a little old-fashioned, and I have never taken kindly to the modern innovation in evening dress adopted by my brethren. My father was a parson and he habitually wore ordinary evening dress, and I followed him in this particular. I think I shall have to get a dog collar and satin stock after all."

The lady did not care whether he did or not. She felt she had wasted an evening.

CHAPTER TWELVE—A CLOSE CORPORATION

I.   —TROLLOPE'S MRS. PROUDIE

N O ONE WHO HAS LIVED FOR ANY length of time in a cathedral town can fail to appreciate the perfection of Anthony Trollope's Barchester series of novels. In my opinion no more artistic achievement than the creation of Barchester and its people exists on the same scale in the English language. I do not think that there is a false note in any scene—a crude tone in any character. Certainly no writer ever dealt with the members of any profession with such completeness and without ceasing to interest a reader from page to page, from chapter to chapter, from volume to volume. Fancy any writer venturing upon five long novels with all the chief characters solicitors or solicitors' wives and daughters! Fancy a dozen medical men stethoscoping their way through a thousand closely printed pages! We know what military novels we have been treated to from time to time—stuff to send guffaws round every mess-room—as crude as the red of the tunics that gave the marksmen of other armies every chance in the old days.

The personages in *Barchester Towers, The Warden, and The Last Chronicle of Barset* are such finished pieces of characterisation that they strike one as being photographs from life. One feels that the author must have had intimate acquaintance with the originals of his portraits, as well as with their entourage, before he could produce such transcripts from nature.

I suppose there was a good deal of speculation when the Barchester novels were appearing as to the identity of the various cathedral dignitaries. It seems to me that such a "placing" of the people was inevitable. But an example was given me of the artistic way in which Trollope went to work in the case of one of his best remembered characters that let me see what a master of his art he was. I was some years under twenty when *The Last Chronicle* fell into my hands: it was the first novel of Trollope's that I read, so that was the first acquaintance I had with Mrs. Proudie. Before I had got through many chapters I knew that I was listening to the voice of the wife of an Irish Prelate —a lady whose character and temperament had been a twenty years' tradition in the household of which I was a member, and whose reputation had followed her from one city to another. The more I read of the book the more impressed I was that this lady had been the model for Mrs. Proudie in spite of the fact that the two had practically nothing in common—nothing except the essentials that go to make up a character.

Mrs. Proudie was a plain, rather stout little woman, but my Mrs. Proudie was a tall, slight, and undoubtedly beautiful woman, even when middle-aged

—the most perfect type of the traditional aristocrat. It would have been impossible for her to do any of the pettifogging of Trollope's vulgar person, in the way that Mrs. Proudie did it, but it was quite clearly understood—by no one better than the Bishop himself—that she was the ruler of the diocese. She was the mother of a family every member of which was remarkably good-looking; but Trollope laid emphasis upon the commonplace daughters of the Proudies.

Only an artist of the highest rank could create a character such as Mrs. Proudie from the suggestions he had derived from the rumours respecting our Bishop's wife, and only an artist of the highest rank could create a personage which compelled all readers who knew the original to recognise the source of his inspiration and feel certain of its identity in spite of the absence of all outward marks of identification.

For several years after reading the Barchester series I was accustomed to hear people in the neighbourhood in which I lived refer to the Bishop's wife as Mrs. Proudie—several clergymen certainly did so; but quite fifteen years had passed before I heard that, previous to his writing *Barchester Towers*, the author had been stationed in the same neighbourhood as an Inspector in the Post Office Department.

"In those days," said my informant, who had served under Trollope, "the Bishop's wife was at the height of her fame. Every one was talking about her and the way she kept the poor Bishop under her thumb. We expected that Mr. Trollope would make something out of her."

When I asked him how he could reconcile the difference between Mrs. Proudie and the other lady—how he could reconcile Mrs. Proudie's death in *The Last Chronicle* with the other's still active life, he told me that he had never read any of Trollope's books: the only writings of Trollope that had come under his cognizance were the official reports which he made to the head of the Department!

Beautiful to the last, and ruling to the last, *our* Mrs. Proudie survived the published record of the other Mrs. Proudie by nearly thirty years. I write this chapter sitting on a sofa which I bought out of the Palace. The fact that the receipt of my cheque was signed by the Bishop and not by the lady, suggests that in financial matters his lordship was permitted to discharge the humblest of clerical duties.

In Broadminster there has never been a rumour of a Mrs. Proudie; but occasionally there comes a discordant note from the belfry of the Cathedral. Only a quick ear can detect it, but having detected it, one is conscious of an impression of uneasiness, and asks oneself or anybody else if it is possible that all is not well in the Close.

What sounds like the merest tinkle of discord outside Broadminster reverberates throughout the Close, causing uneasiness and even perturbation at times.

During the past three years there have been two threatenings of huge upheavals in Minster circles. The rumblings of an earthquake were heard by some people of acute hearing, and the local seismometer—her name is Lady Birnam—foretold a cataclysm. But happily the centre of the disturbance passed away in another direction, and the foundations of the Cathedral remained intact.

II. —THE INNOVATORS

The volcanic force which caused all the alarm was a young clergyman who, by reason of his personal merits and his relationship to the Dean, became the most minor of all the canons, and probably the most pleasing. But before he had been a year in attendance it was rumoured that he had views, and no clergyman with views had ever been associated with the services at the Minster. There have been clergymen who took a lively interest in landscape photography—even colour photography—and others who had rubbed with their own hands some of the finest monumental brasses in the country. A prebendary went so far in horticulture as to stand godfather to a new rose (h.p.), and a precentor who devised an automatic reel—a fishing-rod reel, not the terpsichorean—but no dignitary had previously been known to develop views on the lines adopted by this Canon Mowbray, for his views had an intimate connection with the Church Service.

He had been heard to express the opinion that it was little short of scandalous that people should enter the Cathedral and find themselves surrounded by beauties of architecture and facing combinations of colour in glass that were extremely lovely—that they should be able to hear music of the most elevating type efficiently rendered by an organist of ability and a well-trained choir, but the moment a member of the Chapter—one of the dignitaries of the Church—began to discharge his duties, either in his stall, at the electern, or in the pulpit, the congregation were subjected to an infliction of mediocrity sometimes verging on imbecility. It was little short of scandalous, he said, that the most highly paid functionaries—men whose education had cost a great deal of money—should show themselves so imperfectly equipped to discharge their simplest duties in an intelligent manner. Few of them could even intone correctly, and he had a suspicion that intoning was invented to conceal their deficiency in reading the prayers. When they stood at the lectern and read in that artificial voice that they assumed for the Lessons for the day, treating the most splendidly dramatic episodes with a tameness that suggested rather more than indifference, they proved their inefficiency as plainly as when they stood at the altar-rails and repeated the Commandments in that apologetic tone they put on, as if they hoped the people present would understand quite clearly that they, the readers, were not responsible for the bad taste of the compiler of the Decalogue in referring to offences of which no well-bred lady or gentleman would be guilty.

And then he went on to refer to the preaching....

Now Canon Mowbray did not give expression to his views all at once. He was forced to do so by the action of the Dean and Chapter after he had startled them all, and the congregation as well, by his dramatic reading of the First Lesson, which was of the discomfiture of the Priests of Baal by the prophet Elijah—a subject treated very finely by Mendelssohn.

The truth was that Canon Mowbray had paid a visit to London every week in order to get a lesson in elocution from a well-known ex-actor, and at the end of six months had mastered, at any rate, the fundamentals of the art. His performance, regarded by itself, would have been thought quite creditable; but, judged by comparison with the usual reading of the Lessons in the Minster, it was startling—thrilling. Long before he had got to the ironic outburst of the prophet, "Cry aloud, for he is a god," he had got such a hold upon his hearers that when he made a little pause the silence was striking. At the close also, when he had shut the Book and stood for a few moments before saying, "Here endeth the First Lesson," the silence was the ecclesiastical equivalent to the plaudits of the playhouse at the effective close of an act: he might have said, "Here endeth the First Act."

It seemed as if there was not a sirloin in Broad-minster over which the performance was not discussed. Sides were taken in almost every household of faith, some people condemning the innovation, others being enthusiastic in its favour. The one said it was too theatrical—it was not for clergymen to put themselves into a part, as if they were actors; the other affirmed that the Bible should be read by a clergyman as if he believed what he was reading, not in that *voix blanche,* as the French call the insincere monotone which for some reason, hard to discover, has been almost universally adopted as the voice of the Church.

As a natural consequence of the discussion the attendance at the afternoon service was immense, for it was understood that Canon Mowbray was to read one of the Lessons. Men who had become quite lax in their churchgoing looked up their silk hats, and even chapelgoers, having heard of the morning performance, hastened to the Minster just to see how theatrical it was. The organist wished he had chosen a more showy anthem than "In Judah is God known." This was quite too commonplace for such an occasion, he thought: it would allow of the clergy's competing with the choir for popularity, the idea of which was, of course, absurd.

The offertory was nearly double that of any afternoon of the year.

There could be no doubt that the "draw" was Canon Mowbray. He filled the stage, so to speak; when he went to the lectern the effect was the same as is produced on a full house by the entrance of the "star," and once again the silence was felt to be a subtle form of applause.

Canon Mowbray had no chance of electrifying his hearers, for they were expectant; he managed, however, to get far more out of an unemotional chapter than had ever been got out of it before, so that it was made perfectly clear to every one that he meant to pursue the line he had struck out for himself, and for the next few days there was no real topic in Broad-minster but the innovation of Canon Mowbray.

It was not surprising that the Close should be greatly perturbed by the innovation. The Chapter was against it to a man. They had got into a groove so far as the church services were concerned, and they had been running very easily in it for many years. Where was the need to make any change? they asked. But even if some change was needed, why should it be such a one as that of which Canon Mowbray had made himself the exponent? There were the weaker brethren to consider: in every clerical discussion the question of considering the weaker brethren plays a prominent part. The weaker brethren objected very strongly to the introduction of elocution in any florid form at the lectern or in front of the altar-rails, and beyond a doubt the playhouse—a theatre is invariably alluded to as a playhouse by people who are arguing against it—the playhouse and the House of God are separate and distinct, and any attempt to introduce the atmosphere of the former into the latter savoured of irreverence, and should not be tolerated by any one having at heart the welfare of the Church.

Of course, Canon Mowbray was quickly made aware of the opinion of the Chapter regarding his innovation, and then it was that he made use of the somewhat intemperate phrases already quoted in defining the artistic incompetence of the clergy; and the clergy speedily learned all that he had said and was still saying about them, and they were naturally very much displeased.

But what could they do in the matter?

Well, it was obvious that they could be cold to him—they could delete his name from the list of invitations to their whist parties and dinner parties and luncheon parties. They could make it difficult for him to get up a set at lawn-tennis or badminton; and, sure enough, they put in motion all the apparatus of excommunication which is still at the command of the Church. But the result was not all that had been anticipated; for the people who felt that they owed Canon Mowbray a good turn for the entertainment with which he had provided them for several Sundays, got up special parties in his honour: dinner parties, and whist parties, and even "tweeny" parties—the Sunday lunch between the services at the Cathedral which occupies so prominent a position in the convivial régime of Broadminster. But Canon Mowbray was wise enough not to accept any of the invitations that he received. He knew that there was far more to be got out of a pose as persecuted reformer than from appearing at the most elaborate tweeny lunch that the most interesting house in the town could provide.

He was quite right; for within a month he was summoned before the Dean himself, and remonstrated with on the error of his excessive elocution. It was understood the great Dignitary had used his own weapons against him during this interview: his elocution was excessive as he referred to the Canon's attempt to introduce an element into the services which had previously been monopolised by the playhouse—the Dean, of course, called the theatre the playhouse.

It need scarcely be said that this interview of remonstrance represented a martyr's crown of 22 carats, hall-marked, to Canon Mowbray, and he took care to display it: he never appeared in public without it. He brushed his hair to accommodate its rim upon his head—every one who has come in contact with a martyr knows how far the brushing of his hair goes to the establishment of his claim to the crown—and it was understood that even if Canon Mowbray's "size" had been in excess of that marked on the ticket in his hat, it was nearly certain that within a short time his head would be found quite equal to the wearing of his crown without any one suggesting that it was a misfit.

But he had got the better of the Dean in the interview—he took care that this fact became known. He had not forgotten himself or his position for a moment. He had expressed his great regret that the Dean was unable to look at the question of the innovation with his, the Canon's, eyes; he had a great respect for the Dean's opinion on most matters, and he knew no one whose advice he would follow more gladly; but in this particular point he found it impossible to do so. Surely if the art of the musician was admitted into the services, the art of the elocutionist should not be excluded—and so forth. Good taste? He was said, that he could not allow any considerations of what some people called good taste to interfere with what he believed to be his duty. After all, good taste and bad taste were merely relative terms. It was not possible that on any aesthetic grounds Mr. Dean would be prepared to say that the slovenly reading of the Sacred Word to which they had been for long accustomed at the Minster was more tasteful than—than one in which the ordinary principles of elocution were observed.

It was when the Dean was confronted with arguments which he made no attempt to answer that he became grossly personal, Canon Mowbray said, attributing to him, the Canon, motives unworthy of a clergyman with any sense of his high calling, and thereby proving pretty conclusively, the Canon thought, that as an arbiter of good taste the Dean could scarcely be admitted to a position of any prominence.

The result of the Dean's remonstrance was to strengthen the Canon's cause in the eyes of his adherents; and when one of these friends wrote a letter to the newspapers, expressing the opinion that if Canon Mowbray had been guilty of any breach of discipline the ecclesiastical authorities should take action with a view to justifying themselves in the attitude they had assumed in regard to him, the general opinion was that the Canon had triumphed, for the Dean and Chapter knew perfectly well that they had no power to accept the challenge implied in the letter: the question was not one of turning to the east or turning to the west, or of lighting candles in a place where no artificial illuminant was required, or of wearing an overelaborate robe—it was solely a question of taste, and the discipline of the Church has nothing to do with matters of taste.

It was at this point that Lady Birnam, who claimed to be a local ecclesiastical seismometer, so to speak, prophesied a cataclysm that would shake the Church to its foundations. She went far beyond the advisory committee of St. Paul's in considering the consequences of making new subways by the London County Council.

III.   —THE PEACEMAKERS

And yet within a couple of months the last rumble of the threatened disturbance had passed away.

This is how the *status quo ante bellum* was restored:

The offending Canon was in the habit of confiding in his supporters his feeling of sorrow that none of his clerical brethren had the manliness to follow his example and read the Lessons as they should be read: he had quite believed, he said, that in a short time the slovenly, monotonous reader would have ceased to appear at the lectern; he was greatly disappointed.

But one Sunday an elderly Prebendary astonished every one by "putting on" two separate and distinct voices in reading the First Lesson. It was the chapter in which Moses pleads for the Children of Israel when their destruction is threatened by the Almighty. Now it will be plain to any one that to treat this duologue in an elocutionary style requires a delicacy of touch of the rarest sort; but unhappily the reader seemed to have the idea that all that was necessary to deal with the most important passages effectively was to deliver them in two voices, and this scheme he adopted. The one voice was that of a good-natured gentleman taking the part of naughty schoolboys who had been caught robbing the orchard of an irascible old farmer; the second voice was that of the irascible old farmer who had cornered them and had sent one of his staff for a dog whip.

The effect was startling at first. It seemed as if the clergyman had seen Irving in *The Lyons Mail"* and thought he could not improve greatly upon the method of the actor in the dual rôle—speaking in the mild accents of the amiable Lesurges on the one hand and in the gruff staccato of Dubose on the other. At first this touch of realism was startling, but as it went on it became queer, then funny, and at last it had the element that made its emphatic appeal to most hearers, that of burlesque. Some of the congregation were shocked: they had no idea that "God spake these words and said" in the tone of a testy old gentleman. Others were frankly amused and showed it without reticence; and the entertainment closed with the giggling of choir-boys.

The Second Lesson was read by Canon Mowbray in a very subdued way. Contrary to the expectation of a good many people, he made no attempt to match himself in realistic effects against the Prebendary; and when during the week remarks were made in his hearing respecting that member of the Chapter and his elocution, he only shook his head sadly. The other members of the Chapter could do no more. When an elderly clergyman has made a fool of himself within the precincts of his church people can only shake their heads.

But the next Sunday the congregation who crowded the Minster at the afternoon service shook not only their heads but their bodies also in their decorous but wholly ineffectual attempts to smother their laughter while the Prebendary read a chapter in the Book of Ruth which necessitated, he thought, full orchestral treatment. He clearly saw the parts for a basso, a tenor, a soprano, and a contralto, and he set himself about doing all four by subtle modulations of his voice. Now, people do not as a rule mind a middle-aged parson's putting on a gruff voice when reading what a man said, or going up an octave or so when assuming the dialogue of a milder-mannered man; but when he puts on a falsetto, and a very high falsetto, when he essays to reproduce the words of a woman, and occasionally breaks in an attempt to lay the emphasis on the right words, the most decorous of folk will either laugh or weep—and the great majority of the worshippers in the old Minster this day did the former. Quite a number hurried from the Sacred Fane with their handkerchiefs held close to their mouths. But once outside——

That was how the scandal which threatened to make Broadminster Chapter a house divided against itself was dispersed. It was obvious that the Minster was too antique a place to be made the scene of so great an innovation as Canon Mowbray had attempted to introduce, and he at once fell back into the recognised monotone, with a suspicion of the sing-song rising and falling from sentence to sentence in his reading of the Lessons, and the Prebendary once more followed his example; and so the plague—or worse—was stayed.

But the general impression that prevailed throughout Broadminster when the whole question of the innovation was discussed was that that middle-aged Prebendary had not gone very far in making a fool of himself. They had heard of a potent form of argument technically known as *reductio ad absurdum*, but they had never before had so signal an instance of its successful operation.

IV.   —THE VOX HUMANA

Some years had passed before there was another little fluttering in the Minster dovecotes; but this time the disturbing element happily did not arise within the Chapter. The fact was that at the afternoon service one Sunday a voice of extraordinary charm was heard when the first of the hymns was begun. It was the voice of a professional soprano, and one of the finest *timbre* beyond doubt; but it was so clear and so resonant that, to make use of the verger's criticism whispered into my ear, it gave the rest of the congregation no chance whatsoever. Now every one knows that there is nothing so startling in a church as one voice ringing out even a single note above the vague cloud of sound, if one may be allowed such a phrase, that comes from a singing congregation. But here was a young woman who went through every verse of the hymn as though the volume of sound coming from the nave, the aisle, and the choir itself were only meant as a sort of background for her voice.

Of course before the third stanza was reached the great majority of those who had been singing had ceased. They saw that, in the verger's phrase, they had no chance against so brilliant a vocalist; they turned their eyes upon the young woman, some of them with frowns of indignation, but others with frank admiration. But undoubtedly all were startled.

When the second hymn began it was plain that the music presented no difficulties to the stranger; she sang as before with exquisite sweetness and expression, but still with a ringing clearness that suggested the song of the skylark soaring above a field of corncrakes. Even the efforts of the choir did not rise much above the melody of the corn-crakes in early dawn when that girl was singing.

Naturally such an unusual display caused a considerable amount of talk in Minster circles. It was pronounced in many directions to be in extremely bad taste for any young woman to sing down a whole congregation in such a way; but while some people said it must be put a stop to at once, others declared that they had never had such a treat in their lives. (They probably meant for the expenditure that was represented by their donations to the offertory.)

But when the wives of such members of the Chapter as were blessed with wives declared definitely that a stop must be put to so unreasonable a display of an undoubted gift, their husbands asked how they proposed to put a stop to it; and once again it appeared that, after all, the powers of a Cathedral Chapter are very limited.

Inquiries were made as to who the singer actually was; but no one seemed to know her. She was a stranger, and was certainly not living in the town.

The next Sunday brought about a repetition of the same rather embarrassing scene. The vocalist, who was a very handsome and an expensively but not showily dressed young woman, sang as before quite unconcernedly, and apparently oblivious of having done anything out of the common.

At the end of the first hymn, however, the organist's boy was seen to approach her, and to put a piece of paper into her hand. It obviously contained a message to which an answer was required, for the boy waited while she read the thing, and then she inclined her head, evidently signifying her assent to whatever suggestion it conveyed to her.

No one who saw the act doubted that the organist had sent her a message, begging her not to sing quite so loud.

In due course the precentor announced that "the anthem is taken from Job xix. verses 25, 26: 'I know that my Redeemer liveth... and though worms destroy this body, yet in my flesh shall I see God.'"

The lovely notes of the organ obbligato were heard in the introduction, and then the people in the church became aware of the fact that the melody was not being sung by the usual choir-boy, but by the stranger; and never before had it been sung with such feeling or such an appreciation of its beauty. It was natural that the old Cathedral-goers should look at one another with startled eyes at first—here was an innovation indeed!—but before long the most hardened of them all had yielded to the exquisite charm of the girl's voice, and when the triumphant notes rang out there was no one who remained unmoved under that ancient canopy of Gothic arches.

And that unhappily is the end of the whole story. The girl and the elderly lady who had come with her to the Minster walked away at the close of the service, and no one was able to say in what direction they went or whence they had come. No one in the town knew either of them. They had not been at any hotel, nor had they taken the train to London—the organist made it a point to be at the station to find out. That beautiful, singer might have been a celestial visitant sent as a special compliment to the organist of the Minster— it was rumoured that the views of the organist were strongly in favour of this theory—so mysteriously had she come and so utterly had she vanished.

But during the week that followed that episode in the Minster little else was talked of in the town. The Chapter took the gravest view of the action of the organist in sending that note to the vocalist, asking her if she would kindly sing the solo: he confessed that he had done so. They said that it was quite irregular, and he acknowledged this also; in fact, he was ready to acknowledge every thing to which the Chapter took exception if they would in turn acknowledge that he had been instrumental in providing them with such an artistic treat as they had never known within the walls of the Cathedral. And then he began to laugh at them, for he knew that they all had a wholesome dread of him, from the Dean down. He broached that suspicion about the angel, and lectured them upon the good fortune of some people who had entertained angels unaware. He wondered if that mysterious vocalist had entertained them. If so, he hoped that they would contrive when intoning the prayers in future to end up within a tone or two of the note on which they had started.

"THEY ALL HAD A WHOLESOME DREAD OF HIM"

They smiled and were silent. Some of them thought that he had let them off easily enough. They were trembling lest he should go into particulars.

But for that week there was a great deal of controversy in Church circles respecting the episode, and on the following Sunday the Minster was crowded; for it was rumoured that the organist had another anthem with an effective soprano solo which he meant to spring upon the Chapter in place of the baritone, "What is man that Thou art mindful of him?" which was on the board, in view of the reappearance of the girl.

Every one was disappointed, however; the service was conducted as usual, for the soprano was not there, and Mr. Stone, the very capable baritone, had it all his own way in respect of the anthem. He never sang it better in all his life, and everybody went home disappointed, except perhaps the Chapter and their womenfolk, who had perceived how easily a vocalist of exceptional ability may in certain circumstances be the means of causing confusion in the conducting of the services of the Church.

V.   —THE PILGRIM'S PROGRESS

I am inclined to think that the people of Broad-minster are about the best informed of all people in the county in regard to general topics. But sometimes this opinion, which so many visitors form, is not confirmed by residence in the town. In these days, when one hears that it is impossible to educate a girl as she should be educated for less than £200 a year, one expects a great deal of knowledge from girls generally. A clergyman of the town, who is not connected with the Minster, is constantly telling me of instances that have come under his notice of the most expensively educated girls showing an amount of ignorance that should, but probably would not, make a Board School girl blush were it brought home to her. He assured me that the daughter of one of the Minster dignitaries, in seeing a casual reference to Elaine, had begged him to tell her in which of Shakespeare's plays she appeared: she herself had made a diligent search through that author without success.

I could scarcely believe that such an incident had taken place, for I was under the impression that Tennyson was still read by girls; but a short time afterwards I overheard a couple of young women—one of them not so very young—talking on literature.

The elder had mentioned that she had read in a magazine that the best account of the great plague was in a book written by Defoe, and she wondered if the other girl knew what book it was in. The other shook her head, saying—

"You need not ask me; the only book of Defoe's that I ever read was *The Pilgrim's Progress*, and I never finished it."

"I thought you might chance to know," said the other complacently, evidently not seeing her way into any side issue in respect of the authorship of *The Pilgrim's Progress*. "I'm tremendously interested in something I have been reading on tropical diseases, and I thought that I should like to learn something about the old plagues."

I fancy that both young women went through a course of English literature at their expensive school, and they probably would reply to your assurance that you knew the difference between Daniel Defoe and John Bunyan and their works when you were twelve years of age, that they could have done the same. What chance has Defoe against golf or Bunyan against badminton. If a girl only puts her heart into it she can forget between eighteen and twenty-four much that she has learned previously—at a cost of a couple of thousand pounds or thereabout.

But, I repeat, there is a great deal of intelligence to be found in all circles in Broadminster, and now and again one is confronted by some strong piece of evidence of original investigation on a historical as as well as a literary subject. Seldom, however, does one have an important logical conclusion to an apparently trivial incident enforced upon one with the same lucidity as characterised a lady's expression of surprise that the hallucinations of the great Duke of Wellington in the latter years of his life had not been commented on by any of his biographers. People were accustomed to laugh at the assertion of the Prince Regent that he had been present at the battle of Waterloo, and at the Duke's reply to him when appealed to for confirmation: "Indeed, I have frequently heard your Royal Highness say so." But what about the Duke's own hallucination? Is it not recorded of him that upon one occasion, when watching the playing fields at Eton, he declared that the battle of Waterloo had been fought there? Yet although everyone knew that Waterloo was in Belgium, no one seemed to have noticed the extraordinary mental lapse on the part of a man who might reasonably be supposed to have the chief features of the locality impressed upon him. She added that she feared, if the error were not pointed out in time, the Duke's statement might become generally accepted, and so posterity might be led to believe that Napoleon's career had been brought to a close on the banks of the Thames, which was not a fact.

VI.—THE ATMOSPHERE OF THE MINSTER

The effect of residing for some time in such a town as Broadminster—a community on which the shadow of an ancient Minster has rested for nearly six hundred years—is noteworthy. One breathes of the atmosphere that clings about the old stonework, and, in time, one is conscious of one's ideas and aspirations becoming assimilated with the traditions of the place. On a fine morning in summer even an Irishman feels himself to be an English Conservative—a genuine Tory of the good old days when boys were taught to touch their hats to a "passon," and when it was a matter of common knowledge that the finest vintage ports were reposing in the cellars of the Close.

An instance of the insidious influences of an atmosphere too strongly charged with Anglozone—one must invent a word to express this particular elixir of the cathedral town—came under my notice some years ago. A young American lady, after travelling about a good deal, settled in a beautiful old house in Broadminster. Rooms panelled with old oak, an oak staircase with well-carved newels and finials, and a room on the wall of which some frescowork of the fourteenth century had been discovered, completed the charm which the Minster bells began in the mind of the young woman, and she began to speak English as incorrectly as if she had been born in England.

I met her one day wearing mourning—not exemplary mourning, but enough to induce a mild and conventional expression of sympathy.

Oh no, it was not for any near relation, she said; but surely I had forgotten that the day was the anniversary of the execution of the Earl of Strafford. What Strafford was that? Why, of course, Charles the First's Strafford. How could Englishmen be so neglectful of the memory of one of the greatest of Englishmen?

"If you go into mourning for Strafford, I suppose you fast upon the anniversary of the death of Charles the First?" I suggested.

"The martyrdom of King Charles is commemorated in some parts of the States in the most solemn manner," she replied. "Oh yes, I can assure you that we are Stuart in every fibre of our bodies. I am President of the White Rose Society of Chillingworth County, Massachusetts."

"But you are not, I hope, active Jacobites?" said I.

"Well, no—not just yet; but we can never acknowledge the Hanoverian succession. We owe the Hanoverians a grudge: it was a king of that house who brought about our separation from Great Britain. That old wound rankles still."

CHAPTER THIRTEEN—AMONG THE AMATEURS

I.   —MR. BARTON'S HIGH NOTE

THE ARTISTIC INFLUENCES OF A CATHEDRAL with a good organist and a capable choir in any town cannot be questioned; and so it is that the concerts which take place with some frequency in Broad-minster and the neighbourhood are usually quite good. The members of the choir are always ready to sing for the many deserving objects that occur to the active minds of the organisers of amateur concerts. One of these ladies, however, made up her mind that people were getting tired of the local tenors, and resolved to introduce a new amateur, whom she had heard sing at Brindlington, for a concert she was getting up for the Ophthalmic Hospital. This gentleman's name was Barton, and he was said to be a very promising tenor of a light quality. He certainly behaved as such when he came to Broadminster to rehearse on the afternoon of the day preceding the entertainment. Dr. Brailey, the organist of the Minster, had kindly consented to play the accompaniments as usual, though his best tenor was to be superseded by the gentleman from Brindlington, and he attended the rehearsal.

Before he had got through the first stanza of the stranger's contribution—a song that the musician had accompanied hundreds of times—he found himself being instructed by Mr. Barton how to play the introduction to the second stanza. Then he found himself told that he was playing too loud: "Keep it down, my dear sir, keep it down—this is not a pianoforte solo," said the amateur petulently, to the horror of everyone present, with the exception, apparently, of the musician; for Dr. Brailey only smiled and remarked that he hoped he would with practice be able to give the gentleman satisfaction. But even this course of suavity did not seem to produce a good impression upon the amateur: he continued grumbling, winding up by saying—

"Oh, well, I suppose that will have to do," while he turned his back upon the musician.

But the musician did not seem in the least hurt. He smiled.

He was in his seat at the piano the next evening when the new tenor came forward to sing his song. It occupied, of course, the best place in the programme, and the first stanza came off very well: the high note a bar or two from the close was in itself a feat, but the singer produced it correctly and hung on to it as long as he could, and Dr. Brailey gave him every latitude, not proceeding with the accompaniment until he had quite finished with it.

And then Dr. Brailey did a thing which he alone in the town could do: he raised the key a tone in attacking the second stanza without the singer being aware of it; it was only when he approached the same high note to which he had clung in the first stanza that he began to feel that he was not so much at his ease in forcing it again. He pulled himself together, however, and just managed to touch it—there was no thought of clinging to it now; he touched it and then hurried away from it down the scale, and under covert of the encouraging applause which the singer received the accompanist unostentatiously raised the key again as he dashed into the third stanza. Gratified by his previous success, the tenor went gallantly onward; again he realised that the high note would tax him to the uttermost—he felt that he was straining his voice to touch even a lower note. But what could he do? The copy of the song which he held trembled in his fingers; then he took a quick breath and made a dash for the high note.

He never reached it—his voice broke upon it with the usual comical effect, and the young people in the audience yelled with laughter. A boy scout or two at the back of the hall thought the moment a propitious one for showing how accomplished they were in imitating the everyday sounds of the farmyard; and under such a volley, mingling with the laughter of the choir-boys, one of whom simulated the tremolo of a cat unable to fulfil its engagements in good time, and attempting to produce Chopin's Funeral March from the beginning with a far too meagre orchestra, the singer turned and almost fled from the platform.

It was Dr. Brailey who had to announce to the audience at the start of the second part of the concert that Mr. Barton, owing to a sudden indisposition, would be unable to sing "Let me like a Soldier fall"—the other song that was opposite his name on the programme—but that their old friend, Mr. Stamford, had kindly stepped into the breach and would do his best with that number.

"Loud and prolonged applause," the *Gazette* stated, followed the announcement; for Mr. Stamford was the leading tenor of the Minster choir.

Mr. Barton, carrying with him his three encore songs—he had come fully prepared to meet the preposterous demands of an enthusiastic audience—left Broadminster by the night train. And up to this day I believe that he does not know by what diabolic trick on the part of some one he made such a fiasco. He has been heard to declare that no persuasion will ever induce him to sing again in Broadminster, and, so far as I can gather, there is no likelihood of any machinery being set in motion to cause him to break his vow.

I think that the claim which the musical fraternity of Broadminster advance respecting the moral tone of their performances, whether given under the patronage of the Church or not, can certainly be maintained. The Kreutzer Sonata has been placed on the *Index Expurgatorius* of the Concert Committee ever since Tolstoi wrote a foolish book pointing out whither that composition was likely to lead young people with a tendency toward voluptuousness; and when a lady of a sensitive nature but an open mind submitted to them a song which she had been advised to sing at a forthcoming concert, pointing out where in one line the writer of the words had, she thought, gone a little too far, they considered the matter with closed doors and all females excluded, and decided that her suspicions were but too well founded, and that the offensive line should be altered. This was done, and the honour of Broadminster was preserved intact.

The name of the song was, "It was a Dream," and the line objected to was —

> "We kiss'd beneath the moon's cold beam."

The shock of this shameless confession was mitigated by the substitution of the word "met" for "kiss'd"—

> "We met beneath the moon's cold beam—
>
> It was a dream—it was a dream!"

"Nothing could be happier than the change," said Lady Birnam. "It left so much to the imagination."

II.   —THE MUSICAL TABLEAUX

Some people have been heard to affirm that there is too much music going on at Broadminster. There may perhaps be some grounds for the assumption. At any rate, it is certain that of late few concerts contributed to solely by local talent have paid their expenses. The opinion seems to be general that when the vocalists can be heard every day of the week free of charge in the Minster, people are unwilling to pay three shillings, two shillings, or even (back seats, unreserved) one shilling for listening to them at a concert.

Some time ago, however, when the annual Coal Fund was started, it was absolutely necessary to get up a concert to make a contribution to this excellent charity; and Lady Birnam undertook the direction of the affair.

After consultation with some friends from a distance who were supposed to have sounded all the depths of schemes for the relief of "deserving objects," she came to the conclusion that music, illustrated by *tableaux vivants*, offered the greatest lure to the public. Such a combination had never been attempted in the town, and its novelty would make an appeal to the jaded palates of a concert-ridden community.

The plan of illustrating the music was quite a simple one. Certain dramatic songs were selected and scenery painted to form a suitable background for the episode treated in each; an illustrative group was arranged against such a background, and when the curtain was raised after the singing of each stanza it was like looking at the pictorial cover of the song itself.

For instance, in "The Village Blacksmith" the baritone sang the first stanza, up went the curtain, and there appeared on the platform a living picture of the smith, brawny arms and all, in the act of raising a hammer to strike a very red-hot horseshoe. The next stanza sung was that which referred to the children looking in on the smithy, and when it was sung a charming picture was displayed of immaculate children standing around the door, while the smith neglected his work to pat them on the hair. The third tableau showed the interior of a church with the smith in the family pew raising his eyes pathetically as he hears his daughter's voice in the choir.

The idea seemed a very pleasing one, and it had the "draw" of novelty about it. It was found that several good songs lent themselves admirably to illustration by tableaux, and the young men and maidens were pleased to have the chance of posing in aid of a deserving charity. It so happened, however, that Mr. Stamford's mother died only a few days before the date of the first public performance, so that he was forced to remove his name from the programme. He was to sing "She wore a Wreath of Roses," and the three groups that were arranged for the song were expected to be among the most effective of the evening.

Mr. Stamford was very sorry to relinquish his intention of singing, but he promised the Committee to provide the best substitute possible to get, and this was a friend of his who occupied a position in a bank at Mallingham. He promised to communicate with this gentleman and to tell him what he was to do. He was sure to know "She wore a Wreath of Roses." The substitute turned up in good time: there was, of course, no need for a rehearsal! Mr. Stamford had told him what he was to do, he said, and he preferred playing his own accompaniment.

The first two sets of the evening were received with every token of approval by the audience: the songs were "The Village Blacksmith" and Pinsuti's "Night Watch"; and then the charming young lady in mid Victorian dress, and with a wreath of pink roses on her dark hair, posed on the daïs against a suitable background. The signal was given to the tenor, who was seated at the piano behind the curtain. He struck a few chords and began in excellent style.

"Here a sheer hulk lies poor Tom Bowling."

He had actually got to the end of the first stanza before it dawned upon any responsible person that this was not the "Wreath of Roses," and before he could be arrested he had declared that

"Faithful below he did his du-i-ty,
And now-ow he's gaw-aw-en aloft."

Up went the curtain, revealing a refreshing picture of the pretty girl in the muslin dress and the pink wreath, and after the usual interval for applause the curtain fell. Never had the applause been louder: it caused the members of the Committee who were preparing to strangle the singer to lose their heads completely, and the singer was well through the second stanza before they recovered themselves sufficiently to perceive that it was now too late to do anything, and he went on complacently to say that and so on through the simple, pathetic stanza; and then the curtain rose and showed the charming young lady in white satin among her bridesmaids at the door of the church, and once again the applause was rapturous.

"Heavens above! what do the fools mean by applauding?" whispered the chairman of the Committee.

"Let them go on if they please," said some one. "They think that this is Tom Bowling's bride—his fidelity is rewarded, that's the moral illustrated. 'Tom never from his word departed'—there you are, you see. 'His heart was kind and soft,' and the combined virtues have their reward—*vide tableau*."

Then those of the Committee who had some sense of humour hastened into the anteroom to roar with laughter. They were still so engaged when the curtain rose for the third and last time, showing poor Tom Bowling's widow in appropriate garments. Having heard three times that Tom had gone aloft, it would have been ridiculous if any less pathetic scene had been shown to the audience.

The decent interval that elapsed before the applause came showed how deeply affected was the audience.

But the singer at the piano was pounced upon by the Committee and prevented from going on with his song. He protested that he had only sung three verses, and that he was bound to finish it; but the Committee were firm. Not another note would they let him sing, and he retired hurt.

He was questioned in the anteroom as to how on earth he came to sing "Tom Bowling" when Mr. Stamford must have told him that his song was to be "She wore a Wreath of Roses." Did not Mr. Stamford tell him that? he was asked.

"Oh yes, he said that; but I wasn't going to sing that foolish, sentimental rot. Anybody who knows anything about music will agree with me in thinking that 'Tom Bowling' is worth a dozen of the other, and I'm supposed to sing 'Tom Bowling' rather well."

This was the explanation given by the visitor, and it was commented on pretty freely by some of the Committee.

But the consensus of opinion among the audience and the critics was in favour of the belief that the tableaux illustrating scenes in the life of Tom Bowling—and his widow—were the most effective of the whole entertainment.

III.   —THE DRAMA

I t must be obvious to the least experienced that such a community as may be found in an artistic neighbourhood like Broadminster will take kindly to amateur theatricals. There are two dramatic clubs in Broadminster, and their performances are highly appreciated by the members and their friends. The rivalry between the two is quite amicable, for one set of amateurs devote themselves to the lighter forms of the drama and the other to the loftier, and perhaps they might be called without offence the heavier forms. It may be mentioned that the former are the more popular, but those persons who attend the representations of the latter consider themselves the more superior—as indeed they are; otherwise they would have accorded the tribute of a sunny smile to a little bit of dialogue, with accompanying action, which took place in a performance of *King Renes Daughter* which it was my privilege to attend.

At one place the King and the Moorish physician have had a long scene together, for the physician is certainly inclined to be long-winded. They go out together, and a couple of the courtiers enter the garden and express surprise not to find the others waiting for them. One of them says—

"The King is gone, nor can I see the leech."

Now, if the amateur had simply said the words, his meaning, I believe, unless I am over-sanguine, would have been understood. But when, after shading his eyes with a hand while he gazed into the distance of stately trees and saying, "The King is gone," he bent his eyes to the ground and moved a stone or two about with his toe before adding, "Nor can I see the leech," I am inclined to think he puzzled some of his audience.

I had the curiosity to inquire what was in his mind when he sent his eyes roaming about the ground while he grubbed with his feet, and I learned that he thought it would be quite natural for any one searching for a leech to move the stones about to see if it was concealing itself in the earth.

He was evidently under the impression that the wise physician was habitually followed by a pet leech, or perhaps that he had brought it with him to try what effect it would have upon the Princess's eyes, and that it had escaped through a hole in his waistcoat pocket.

CHAPTER FOURTEEN—THE LIGHTER SIDE OF CLERICAL LIFE

I. —THE FRANK CANON

I DO NOT THINK THAT, TAKING THEM all round, the Cathedral dignitaries of Broadminster can be accused of assuming a greater importance than is due to their position; but a story is told about a Canon, lately deceased, which goes far to prove that he at least did not shrink from putting forward what he believed to be a reasonable claim to distinction—relative distinction. It is said that he was in the one bookseller's shop which is still to be found in the town. It was Saturday evening, when a stranger entered and, after buying a book, inquired of the proprietor who was the best preacher in the place: he explained that he was staying over Sunday and was anxious to hear the best.

This was too delicate a question for the bookseller (with a clergyman at his elbow) to answer at a moment's notice; so he thought he would do well to evade the responsibility by referring the stranger to the Canon.

"This gentleman is a stranger to the town, sir," he said, "and he wishes to know who is the best preacher. I thought that perhaps you, sir——"

"I hope you will pardon me, sir," said the stranger. "I am staying here till Monday, and I ventured to inquire who is the best preacher."

"The best preacher, sir?" said the Canon, looking up from the book which he was sampling. "The best preacher? I am the best preacher, sir: I am Canon Hillman."

The stranger was slightly startled.

"Thank you very much, sir," he said quickly. "And who do you consider the next best?"

"The next best is my brother, sir, the Reverend Theophilus Hillman."

The stranger raised his hat and hurried away.

This Canon Hillman had a reputation for that sort of frankness suggested by the story which I have ventured to repeat as it was told to me, and which I have no difficulty in believing, from the example I had of his manner several years ago. I was sojourning at an hotel between Nice and Beaulieu, and he appeared one night at table d'hôte dinner. It was the custom for the proprietor, who, curiously enough, did not speak or understand English, though he was a Swiss, to stand at the entrance to the *salle à manger*, bowing out his guests as they passed into the spacious lounge after dinner, and in returning his courtesy, people said a word or two in commendation of his cuisine, to which he responded with further bows.

It so happened upon this particular night, however, that one or two little mistakes had occurred to mar the harmony of the repast as a whole—they were quite trifles—the *pré salé* being underdone and a jelly not having set with that rigidity which is expected in such comestibles, but which is not always to be found in them.

While we were filing out of the room I was almost immediately behind Canon Hillman, and I heard him grumbling to a man who had been at his table, but who did not seem to sympathise with him; and this went on until they had reached the bowing proprietor, when the Canon stopped.

"I wish to tell you, sir, that I have never eaten a worse dinner at any hotel in my life," he said. "There was not a dish that any one could eat—I consider it simply outrageous."

Not one word did the man understand, for the Canon had spoken in English. The proprietor smiled and bowed most placidly, saying—*"Je vous remercie mille fois, m'sieur—votre compliment est très distingué—très gracieux; je suis heureux—merci!"*

He had too hastily assumed that the clergyman had offered him the usual congratulations upon his cuisine, and he had replied with more than his customary politeness, the visitor having shown himself to be much more enthusiastic than the ordinary run of people had time to be, considering that most of them were counting the moments until they should be in the Casino at Monte Carlo.

I did not know who the very frank clergyman was at that time; but four or five years later I recognised him at Broadminster.

His brother, the second best preacher, assuming the correctness of the Canon's judgment, though perhaps it might have been reversed on appeal, was rector of one of the parishes, and it was rumoured that he was not disposed at any time to take too humble a view of his claims to distinction, however slow other people might be to admit their validity. It is said that upon one occasion, on his return from a visit to the Holy Land, he preached a sermon giving some striking examples of the fulfilment of prophecy in connection with the topography of Palestine.

"My dear friends," he said, "I was particularly struck with the accuracy of some of the details of the prophecies, when one day I was among the ruins of one of those cities referred to in the Sacred Writings. I had the Book in my hand, and I read that the land should be in heaps: I looked up, and there were heaps on every side. I read that the bittern should cry there: I looked up, and, lo, a bittern was standing there in its loneliness. I read that the minister of the Lord should mourn there. My dear friends, *I was that minister.*"

II.   —THE "CHARPSON"

The only clergyman in Broadminster who, so far as I have heard, was fully qualified to take a place in one of the Barchester groups was a person named Gilliman. He was a small, stout gentleman with a comical ruddy face and sparse, bristly grizzly hair. He had no benefice, but was one of those unattached parsons who, in the phrase of the servants' registry office, was ready to "oblige" either by the day or as locum tenens for an absent incumbent. He had been left a small competence by his mother—quite enough for a clerical bachelor to live on, and he was a bachelor. He never sought for a job, but when he got one he proved that he held fast to the excellent precept that the labourer is worthy of his hire. If any brother parson expected that he would take his duty out of love or zeal, that parson left himself open to disappointment. I think he would have made a worthy curate to Mr. Quiverful; but Mr. Quiverful would have felt so chastened in spirit by his proximity that he would have got rid of him within a month.

He was a zealous patron of the amateur, whether musical or dramatic. He could always be depended on to buy one of the cheaper, but never one of the cheapest, tickets for a concert or a comedy, and he seemed as pleased with the most incompetent amateur as with the best. He was socially unambitious; no one seemed to invite him to any function, with the exception of the Dean's annual garden party: he went to this, and so did every one else.

It was not until he had been a resident in Broad-minster for several years that people found out why he had settled in that town. It might be supposed that there were enough clergymen here to serve as a reservoir for all the neighbourhood in an emergency. I once heard an American lady who was on a cathedral tour through Europe say just outside Santa Croce on a feast day: "There are priests to burn in Florence if I do my sums right." Her slang meant that there was a superfluity of the clergy in that city, and perhaps she was right. I will not make use of her slang in referring to Broadminster, but assuredly it might strike anyone that there was a sufficient number of clerics in the purlieu of the Minster to meet the needs of the neighbourhood without making the presence of so accommodating a person as Mr. Gilliman a convenience. In an unguarded moment, however, he confessed to some one that years ago, when he had first come to the town, it was his earnest hope to drop into some vacant stall in the Minster. He had dreams of being appointed to a canonry by some fortunate combination of circumstances, and he had gone on waiting for such an accident, and meantime attending all the amateur performances in the place.

He was a very good preacher, people said who had heard him, and others who had not heard him; but few were aware of how he managed to excel in a direction that seemed just the opposite to the bent of such a man. The truth was that his father had been a zealous rector of a parish in Devonshire, and had bequeathed to him a large sackful of sermons that he had preached to his flock since his ordination; and when the fortunate legatee was called on "to oblige" for an absent cleric, he simply put his hand into the mouth of the sack and drew out a sermon, put it into his pocket, and went away and preached it in due course, dropping it into his sermon sack on his return. Thus it was that people said he preached much better than they expected—and he probably did so; but he could not tell you the next day on what subject he had preached.

That legacy and his impartial system of dealing with it served him in good stead; but upon one occasion it might have caused him to feel some awkwardness if he had not been so completely detached from his duty in the pulpit. The fact was that he had been called away at a moment's notice to take the duty for a clergyman who had knocked himself up by umpiring in a cricket match on a very hot Saturday. He had never been to the place before, so he had to look up trains and connections, and by the time he had got out of this maze the train that he had selected was almost ready to start. He hurried to the faithful sack and pulled out a fat sermon roll, and rushed away for the station.

He was lucky in catching the train and the subsequent connections, and arrived at the church with nearly half an hour to spare. He went through the service and found himself in the pulpit with his sermon opened on the cushion in front of him.

Now it so happened that the discourse which he had drawn in his usual way from the paternal sack was the valedictory sermon preached by his father in the church of which he had been rector for forty years, and there was the son beginning it in a church which he had never seen before that morning!

He was quite unconscious of any want of felicity in his choice. He began the sermon and went through with it, feeling no qualm. He had every confidence in the orthodoxy of his father; he would never get into a scrape through preaching what the dear old man had preached years ago. And so he went onto tell his congregation that more than forty years had passed since he had first stood before them to preach the Gospel of Truth, and that every year of that forty he had stood where he was standing to-day, Sunday after Sunday —that he saw before him aged men and women whom he had known as young men and maidens—that by the favour of Heaven he had lived to baptize the offspring of those whom he had himself baptized in their infancy —yea, unto the third generation he had come, and now he was standing before them for the last time. The hour of parting had come, and would any among them say that that hour was not bitter to them all?

Well, no one did go so far as to assert that the hour was not bitter to them all. I was assured that the congregation were bathed in tears, so affected were they by the thought that the clergyman who had "obliged" for the day was about to vacate the pulpit for ever. They felt the blow deeply—much more deeply than the parson seemed to feel it, for he managed to hold back his tears so long as he was in the pulpit, though his marvellous powers of self-repression may have deserted him an hour later, and he may have broken down utterly in the train when making the return journey; the chances are, however, that he did nothing of the sort, for he had not the remotest idea what the sermon had been about.

And the strangest thing of all in connection with this incident is that the churchwardens expressed themselves as greatly pleased with the sermon, and one of them referring to it the next day in the hearing of my informant, said he had never been so affected in his life as he was under the influence of the sermon, and he hoped that the eloquent clergyman would be able to preach it again in the near future.

It is quite likely that his wish was gratified, though I do not think that any one who had the best interests of the Church at heart would advocate the adoption of the farewell tours system of the popular actor or singer by the clergy. It might hurt the susceptibilities of some members of a congregation to hear a clergyman bid an affecting farewell to a crowd of people who were complete strangers to him, and the sincerity of his sorrow might be called in question when they reflected that an ordinary man can scarcely be broken-hearted at the thought of never seeing again the faces he had never seen before. But that, of course, involves the question of how far the susceptibilities of the weaker brethren should be considered.

My informant, who was present upon the occasion referred to, was also a stranger to the place. He was staying with the doctor's family, and, walking home from the church, the doctor's wife remarked how beautiful the sermon had been.

"Your rector bears his age very well," said her companion. "He does not look a day over forty, and yet, according to his own account, he must be at least sixty-five."

"Our rector? But that clergyman is not our rector," said the lady. "Our rector is ill; the one we had today came to do duty for him. He is a stranger."

"But why, then, should he talk of having baptized half the congregation and married the other half—of never having been absent from the pulpit for forty years and more?" asked the man.

"Oh, you are hypercritical!" cried the lady. "Some latitude should be allowed to clergymen. He only made use of one of the figures of speech of the pulpit."

It is recorded of the same estimable charpson—if a parson who also discharges the duties of a squire has been called a squarson, may not one who goes out like a charwoman by the day be called a charpson?—that upon one occasion he was asked to do duty for an absent clergyman at a village in Hampshire, but the contract was for the morning service only. When he was disrobing in the vestry after preaching the ser mon, a couple of churchwardens approached him on the subject of the evening service also. He said that he would be very pleased indeed to take the evening service, but of course he should have to receive another guinea. The churchwardens demurred. They said they thought that, as he was on the spot——

He shook his head.

"I cannot see that that has anything to do with the case," said the clergyman. "One service and sermon, one guinea; two services and two sermons, two guineas."

The officials agreed that the article was marked in plain figures; but still they thought—— Well, would he consent to take the evening service for another half-guinea?

After thinking over the proposal, the clergyman consented to do so; and then one of the wardens suggested that perhaps Mr. Gilliman would not mind saying just a few words—not a sermon—not a regular sermon, of course, but just a few words—to the congregation after the evening service.

After some further thought Mr. Gilliman said he would have no objection to say a few words in this way, and the wardens thanked him and handed him a sovereign, a half-sovereign, a shilling, and a sixpence. They went so far as to pay him for the evening in advance, to show that they had unlimited confidence in him.

On his part he resolved to prove to them that their confidence in him was not misplaced; so, after reading the evening service, he came to the front of the altar-rails and said—

"Dear brethren, I have been asked to say a few words to you at this time instead of preaching the customary sermon. What I wish to say to each and every one of you whom I see assembled before me—and what I think it is the intention of your churchwardens that I should communicate to you—is that there will be no sermon in this church to-night. Let us sing, to the praise and glory of God, the ninety-second Hymn."

He easily caught the late train to London, though the evening service in respect of trains is much more irregular than that at which he had presided in the church.

The Reverend Herbert Gilliman, B.A.Oxon, never received preferment; but some one remarked to me after his death, when touching on his career, that far less worthy parsons had been appointed to a cure of souls by the patrons of livings, without the parishioners having any voice whatever in the matter.

I agreed with him, and said that I thought they managed these things better in Scotland, where the candidate minister preached once or twice to the congregation to allow of their judging of his powers before they accepted him.

"Yes," he assented. "I think that the application of the hire-purchase system in these matters is highly desirable."

"It's not exactly the hire-purchase system," said a purist in phrases. "It is more of the 'on sale or return' system of business."

"What was in my mind," said a third, "was a tasting order for spirits in bond."

III.   —THE BIBLE CLASS

I prefaced my repetition of passages in the career of the Reverend Herbert Gilliman with an expression of my belief that he was the only cleric in Broadminster who suggested to me one of the slightly shop-soiled clergymen in Anthony Trollope's Barchester novels. Of the ladies of the Close or the ladies of the Palace I have never heard of one who, in the remotest degree, suggested a relationship with Mrs. Proudie.

I have heard, however, of the recent appearance of a lady, who is said to have an intimate acquaintance with the Greek language, at the weekly meeting of the Bible class, presided over by the Dean, who, it is said, has also got some knowledge of the same tongue. The Minster Bible class is one of the most exclusive of lady's clubs. It is understood that no one is eligible for membership who has not been presented at Court—at least so some one, who was not a member, affirmed. Another defined it as a sort of religious Almack's; but it was a man, and a clergyman into the bargain, who said it was an attempt to run an eighteenth-century French salon on Church of England lines.

Without resembling Mrs. Proudie in even the most distant way, the lady of whom I have heard has succeeded, I am told, in changing the whole character of the Bible class—all through her knowledge of Greek. Without being in any way insolent or even self-assertive, she has, I think I am right in stating, openly differed from the interpretation put upon certain passages by the Dean himself; and no human being in Broadminster is recorded to have differed from the Dean on any point whatsoever. But she was a stranger and apparently unacquainted with the best traditions of the town; and, moreover, it was the Dean himself who invited her to join the Bible class. And when she suggests quite a different interpretation of a text from that advanced by the Dean, referring him to certain of the newest "readings" as her authority, he does not seem to be in the least irritated; indeed, on one occasion, when the question arose as to the exact shade of St. Paul's meaning when he made use of the particle $ôi$, the Dean was understood to say that he thought the lady's suggestion well worthy of consideration.

All the higher orders of the clerical establishment—those who are, so to speak, "on the strength" of the Chapter—those to whom the great Lord Shaftesbury would have given, without the reservation of a single finger, his whole hand to shake—are not, however, so meek as Mr. Dean, and it is whispered that two or three of them have recently been keeping the Bible class at a distance, while others, in view of being called on to preside at one of its meetings, have been seen searching on their bookshelves for Liddell and Scott and blowing the dust off the edges.

All the old members of the class are declaring, however, that in future they will make complete ignorance of Greek an essential to membership. The very existence of a Bible class assumes ignorance, and no one has any business to belong to it who is capable of differing from the Dean, or, at least, who is sufficiently tactless to express such a divergence of opinion even though she may be sure of her ground.

Such a show of feeling in this matter goes far to assure Broadminster that there is no chance of Mrs. Proudie being tolerated in the diocese.

When I was walking down the principal street of Broadminster—the street on which the leading silversmith and the leading draper have their premises— there went past a very high carriage. I hesitate to refer to it as "well appointed," this chapter not being one of a novel, and, besides, I do not quite know what is meant by a well-appointed carriage; but the vehicle to which I refer was high, its horses were well matched and good steppers, and the coachman and footman were also a match pair. The young person with whom I was walking bowed to the occupants of the carriage—a young cleric and an extremely goodlooking and well-dressed lady.

"Nice looking people," I ventured to remark. "You know them, it would appear."

"Know them? I should think I do know them: he is our curate," replied my companion, who was, I may mention, the daughter of a clergyman.

"The Church is looking up when curates sit behind high-stepping bays," said I.

"He is the best curate we ever had," said she. "He is the most obliging man ever known. He never grumbles at having to take both services some Sundays and to preach as well—a splendid preacher, too—never longer than a quarter of an hour."

"Anything else?" I inquired.

"Yes," she said slowly and with something of awe in her voice. "He is a one bisquer at croquet!"

I tried to catch sight of the carriage and its bays, but it must have been a mile away by this time.

"And he does all that out of the hundred and fifty pounds a year your father pays him?"

"He does indeed, eked out by the five thousand a year his father left him: his father was Sir Edmund Bonnewell, the great contractor. You have heard of him?"

I had.

IV.   —THE ENCYCLOPÆDIC PARSON

It is impossible that every one should be fully informed on all points even in so enlightened a community as Broadminster; but there is one clergyman who has a reputation for being the most artful fisherman in the Close, and of being always able to answer any question that may be put to him by the most casual inquirer. I heard him discussing the origin of a fire that had taken place in the town a few days before, and, as is usual in these days, it was said to have been due to a short circuit in the electric wires.

"I have often wondered what a short circuit is," said a lady. "Can you tell me what it is, Mr. Tomlinson?"

"A short circuit? Oh, it's very simple," said the fully informed parson. "A short circuit is when—when—oh yes, when it is only a very short way from the electric lamp to where the wire is joined on to the cable."

"And that causes the fire?" she asked.

"Oh, of course—it is bound to, sooner or later."

"I wonder why they don't make it longer then."

"Oh, that's the way they scamp everything nowadays."

Only a few days had passed before I heard him telling another lady of the good luck that had attended the pottering about bookstalls indulged in by a brother parson in a neighbouring town.

"He wrote to me a few days ago, to tell me that he had picked up a genuine 'Breeches' Bible for sixpence," he said; "and only a short time before he bought a fine Aldine for fourpence. What luck!"

"Extraordinary," said the lady. "I'm afraid that I forget what a 'Breeches' Bible is, Mr. Tomlinson." He laughed good-naturedly.

"Pray, what is a 'Breeches' Bible?" she asked coaxingly.

He was quite ready for her.

"A 'Breeches' Bible?" he cried. "Oh, a 'Breeches' Bible is the one that was carried by Cromwell's troopers in their pockets; it was made specially for carrying about—small, you know, and compact. I remember reading that several of the soldiers had their lives saved owing to the bullets having lodged in the volume in their breeches pocket."

"Not really?" said the lady. "How very interesting! I do believe that I heard something like that having happened, I forget where."

I wondered if the Reverend Mr. Tomlinson was not, after all, something of a humourist—if he was not engaged in that delicate dynamic operation known as "pulling her leg." I had good reason to know some time afterwards, however, that there was no foundation for my suspicion in this direction. He spoke what he imagined must be true, and he was too lazy to verify his own conclusions.

When the lady asked him—

"And what might be the real value of one of those Bibles?" he replied—

"Anything from a thousand pounds up. I believe that one was bought by an American a short time ago for over four thousand pounds."

"What! Not really? A thousand pounds?" she cried. "Will you kindly give me his address? I must write to him for a subscription for our new bells."

"For goodness' sake don't tell him that you heard of his good luck from me," cried Mr. Tomlinson.

V.   —THE ALMONERS

THE COTTAGE FATHER

The recognised Church charities of Broadminster are numerous and constantly increasing. To be connected in some way with a charitable organisation seems to offer an irresistible attraction to some people, chiefly ladies; and every now and again a new lady starts up in Church circles with a new scheme of compelling people to accept alms or the equivalent, or of increasing the usefulness of the Church. The amount of time these masterful persons expend in reading papers embodying the most appalling of platitudes of sentiment, and betraying even a more astounding ignorance of political economy than a Chancellor of the Exchequer has ever revealed in a Budget speech, is astounding. All these papers, so far as I can gather, assume that only what their patrons call "the lower classes" stand in need of the reforms they suggest. They take it for granted that a cottage-mother, who has had perhaps thirty years' experience of making a pound a week do duty for twenty-five shillings, stands in need of instruction at the hands of a mansion-mother who cannot keep out of debt with an income of a thousand a year.

If I were a person in authority with a voice in framing the conditions which must be conformed with by all ladies who put themselves forward in the advocacy of some of these great social schemes, I would decree that no lady who uses a tortoiseshell lorgnette with a long handle should be permitted to read a paper, or to receive the *laissez-passer* of any organisation to a house the valuation of which is less than twenty-five pounds a year. As a medium of insulting patronage, nothing that has ever been invented approaches in power this particular weapon in the well-gloved hands of a well-furred, middle-aged lady who studies with some reason all advertisements addressed to those with a tendency to stoutness. (I have gone a long way about to avoid hurting the susceptibilities of any one.)

Only once did I see an attack with this weapon successfully repulsed. There was an extremely pretty girl in the centre of the drawing-room, when a couple of those ladies whose existence I have hinted at entered and immediately began a frontal attack through the glazed tortoiseshell with the long handles, and the little forced smiles that accompanied the movement showed them to be old campaigners. They brought the pretty girl into focus, conning her from head to foot and exchanging whispered comments upon the result of their scrutiny. The girl saw them, and, to paraphrase the poet, they "by tact of trade were well aware that that girl knew they were looking at her"; but that fact had no effect upon them. They continued their scrutiny and their whisperings, and I saw the girl's face become rosy. But then I saw that she was "limbering up" and would go into action in a moment.

She did. She was talking to an elder lady, who might have been her mother, and the latter had one of the same long-handled glasses lying on her muff. In an instant the girl had possessed herself of it, slipped it off its swivel, and was using it precisely as the others were using theirs, only returning their fire, so to speak. Then she whispered something over her hand to her companion, who laughed outright. That was enough for the attacking force: their battery was silenced; but the girl refused to withdraw, and for quite five minutes, I think, they were well aware that her eyes were upon them. Wherever they went they felt that they were still within her range, and that her innocent smile was playing about them. I never saw two more uneasy ladies in my life, and I trust that they learned their lesson.

The most singular point in this connection is that the girl was known to her friends as shy and retiring by nature—a less self-assertive girl could not be imagined. It seems to me that there is a lesson to be learned from this fact in addition to that which it is to be hoped she taught her elders, who certainly did not possess her shyness: it is the lesson of the rousing of a feminine instinct of defence, which is exhibited in another form when the defence is that of offspring. Even the most timid feminine thing will act in direct opposition to its reputed nature when called on to defend its young; and even the most retiring girl may assume an offensive attitude under the provocation of poised tortoiseshell and elevated eyebrows.

But I am pretty sure that that nice girl, when she went home and was alone in her room, sang no song of Miriam as she recalled her triumph. No, if she did not shed some tears at the thought of how she had behaved in so unaccountable away, I am greatly mistaken.

The comedy of the administration of charity has yet to be written; but when such a work is taken in hand I trust that a chapter will be devoted to the self-denying industry of the Misses Gifford. These two elderly ladies are the daughters of a deceased jerry-builder, and they enjoy a large income, the greater portion of which is derived from insanitary house property; and they are devoted to good works, including the amelioration of the condition of the poor. Every year they issue invitations to a show of their good works at their own house, and these are found to take the form of coarsely knitted woollen socks, thick mufflers made of the cheapest materials, petticoats constructed out of blankets that have been consigned to the rag-basket, and aprons out of tablecloths that have been rescued from the dustbin. Some of the articles of clothing seem to represent in themselves the heterogeneousness of a jumble sale, and all are cheap, shoddy, and shapeless. And yet this pair of feminine philanthropists show all comers round the room where they are exhibited with sparkling eyes and faces glowing with proper pride at the result of their industry. They worry the local newspapers for a paragraph that shall make all the world acquainted with their benevolence, and now and again their importunity is rewarded.

What becomes of the conglomeration of horrors which they create in the name of charity no one seems to know; but it is impossible to imagine any self-respecting family so far forgetting what is due to themselves as to wear such things. For themselves, it is well known that the Misses Gifford never forget what is due to them, or to insist on its payment on the day that it becomes due. They have a brother who, without being an active philanthropist, is well worthy of them. He collects the rents from their insanitary tenements, and he does so with a ruthless hand. There is no measure of bluff or bluster of which he is not a master. But there are scores of people in their own town who see the dear old maiden ladies in church and say that they remind them of *Cranford* and *Quality Street!*

But knowing as I did a good deal about them, I was reminded more of an earlier work still in which the devourers of widows' houses were said to be Pharisees as well. Such a pair of feminine Pharisees as those whom I call the Misses Gifford—Gifford is not, of course, their real name—are hardly to be found outside their own town.

CHAPTER FIFTEEN—THE CROQUET LAWNS

I.   —A CONGENIAL PURSUIT

No MENTION OF BURFORD WOULD BE complete unless two-thirds of the account were given over to its croquet ground and its croquet practitioners.

An exhaustive, or even a perfunctory, reference to sport is out of place in any description of the lighter side of life in the provinces, for people in all levels of life take their games very seriously, and croquet, as played nowadays, is the most serious of pursuits. Clergymen who practise it habitually seek for relaxation from the strain its seriousness imposes on them in the pages of the Fathers. It is a matter of common knowledge that a clergyman in charge of a parish in Burford invariably writes out his sermons during the three-ball breaks of his opponents. It is supposed to be *de rigueur* for a player who has let his, or her, opponent 'in' to take no interest whatever in that opponent's strokes when making a break. It is supposed that if you pay any attention to your opponent's play you may put him, or her, off; and so scrupulous are some players lest they should put an antagonist off, they occasionally stroll off the court and return with a bored look only when they are sent for. But the chivalry of the habitual croquet players really knows no bounds. Another of their characteristics is absolutely quixotic. It takes the form of walking off the court as if the game were already finished when an opponent has yet to make three or four hoops before pegging-out; the object of such a move being, of course, to give an opponent more confidence at a critical moment.

It is a doubtful point, however, and I have never heard it decided by a referee, if this object is likely to be effected by a losing player breaking the handle of her mallet across her knee when she has failed to shoot in; though one cannot doubt that only a spirit of self-denial actuates such a player as makes a point of placing in the form of pennies on a chair, at the opposite side of the court from where she sits, the bisques to which her opponent is entitled, thus putting herself to the trouble of walking across, interrupting her opponent's play when the latter had taken a bisque, in order to remove one of the pennies.

The people who sneer at croquet are those who have no knowledge of the game as played nowadays on such courts as there are at Broadminster. There is no more scientific game, nor is there one that demands a more unerring judgment, a steadier hand, or a clearer eye.

Croquet seems to be the ideal game for the freak, the cripple, or the aged.

One of the best players in the neighbourhood is the chaplain to a lunatic asylum. He has a large amount of practice.

During the past few years the champion lawns have been invaded by schoolboys and schoolgirls, with the result that some of the best prizes have been carried off by them.

I cannot imagine a more melancholy sight than that of half a dozen healthy boys, who should be at cricket or lawn-tennis, solemnly and slowly knocking the balls through the hoops and stolidly going through the operations of "peeling," "laying up," "wiring," and the like.

II.   —THE PLAYERS

But even croquet has its lighter moments. I witnessed a match some time ago between a well-set-up cavalry officer (retired with the rank of Major-General) and a cub of a lad—a slouching, hulking fellow whose gait showed that he had never had a day's athletic training. The boy won and went grinning off the lawns. His mother received him with grins, and the General walked away in the direction of the river. It occurred to me that people should keep an eye upon him. But he did not even fling his mallet into the stream.

He turned up a little later at another court, and this time he was victorious.

But against whom?

Against a stout elderly lady crippled with rheumatism; and he just managed to beat her through making a lucky shot!

It seems to me to be marvellous that, with the possibilities of such humiliation before players, any except the decrepit should be found willing to take part in tournaments.

There can be no doubt, however, as to the absorbing power of croquet upon certain temperaments. I have met an elderly lady of Early Victorian proportions who, I am positive, can recollect the details of every match she has ever played. If she were not able to do so she would sometimes be compelled to sit in silence, for to her conversation means nothing beyond a recapitulation of her croquet games. Try her as you may upon other topics, it is no use. She seems intensely bored if you touch upon the theatre, and to music and the other arts she is rather more than indifferent. Indifference might be represented as "scratch," but her attitude can only be represented by a minus sign. On art she should be a -3, on music a -6, and on literature a -20. These are her handicaps, so far as I am capable of judging.

She is the terror of the managers of tournaments, such a hole-and-corner game as she plays. She never leaves anything to chance: she invariably sends herself into a corner. Her most dashing game occupies four hours. It is said that she has strong views on the subject of assimilating the game of croquet with the game of cricket in regard to the duration of a match. If it takes three days to play a cricket match, why should not the same limits be extended to a croquet match? she wishes to know. The reply that is suggested by the people with whom she has played is that even at a three-day match she would complain bitterly that she was hustled by the managers. At present her life seems a perpetual complaint. During the season she grumbles her way from tournament to tournament; and when she seats herself by the side of an unwary person to watch a match, even though it is a final for the cup, she immediately begins to describe one of her games—it may be one that took place five years before—and keeps on giving detail after detail of trivialities, with a complete disregard of the excitements of the court where she is sitting and the applause of the crowd at some brilliant play—on she rumbles, unless her unwilling confidant rises and flies for covert. It takes her even longer to describe one of her games than it does to play it. Her latest complaint is that croquet players are becoming very unsociable, the basis of her charge being that when she approaches a court to sit down and watch a game, the people on the chairs whom she knows quite well get up and go away. She does not believe that in every case they do so, as was suggested, to give her a choice of chairs.

She thinks that those should remain whom she has known for some years. It does not appear ever to have occurred to her that they get up and fly because they have known her for some years.

Another *devotée* has become so absorbed in her cult as to become upon occasions an embarrassment to her relations. Of course no one makes any remark upon a player thinking of nothing besides croquet: it is assumed that a lady who means to become a player will not waste time thinking about anything else.

> "Man's croquet is of man's life a thing apart.
>
> 'Tis woman's sole existence."

That is acknowledged as only reasonable; but it must sometimes be embarrassing to the relations of this lady when at a dinner party she refuses an offered entrée on the ground that she is wired, or when she checks a neighbour for taking a meringue because he or she has previously been playing with the green. It appears quite feasible to me, however, that the green of the salad and the white of the meringue should suggest to a thoughtful croquet player the need for such a caution as is attributed to her on good authority; nor do I think it so very unreasonable that on allowing herself to be carried on a 'bus beyond her destination, through thinking out a croquet problem, she should, on being informed by the conductor that the vehicle went no farther, say—"What a fool I was not to take a bisque sooner!"

It is said that this same lady caused a considerable flutter in a railway carriage one day when she was working out another croquet problem, and was heard to mutter—"Shall I shoot now?"

Any time I chanced to look in at a croquet tournament on the beautiful lawns at Broadminster I came away with a laugh, and upon more than one occasion I found that the laugh was against myself. Long ago I was accustomed to look with a pathetic interest at the reappearance year after year of the beautiful mother of a beautiful daughter at the tournament. Surely, I thought, there could not be a more pathetic sight than that of a mother with a picturesque home and a husband, setting out from both, early in the month of June, when the rosery is becoming a paradise of blossom, and travelling from country town to country town and from one hotel to another, without intermission until October, for the sake of being by the side of a daughter who has given up her life to the game.

The laugh came in when I found that the mother was more devoted to looking on at croquet than the girl was to playing the game! The pathetic figure was really the daughter, who was acting as companion to her mother to enable her with propriety to gratify her passion for watching people play croquet. The daughter complained a little at first, but now she says she has come to see that she should be unselfish and sink her own inclinations so that her mother may have some innocent enjoyment.

She looks very carefully after her mother, and is even able sometimes to exchange a few words with her at intervals during the day's play.

Since I found this out I have never allowed myself to be carried away in pity for one who elects to play the part of onlooker at a game of croquet. People who spend their time looking on at croquet are deserving of no pity.

I have been told that when hospitality is offered to some of the visitors by people in Broadminster during the tournament week, it is now not invariably accepted without caution and preliminary inquiry. A bitter story was imparted to me by a man who had been kindly invited by one of the inhabitants to stay at his house for the croquet week. My friend gratefully accepted, and as the whole of the local family were players, he was brought up to their villa after the first day's play. He found the house a charming one of its class, and he thought himself lucky in his billet. Dinner was served, and then the little rift within the hospitable lute was suggested: there was no wine offered to him! The hissing of syphons round the table gave expression to his views on the subject of such hospitality; but what could he say in reply to his host when the latter turned to him, remarking quite pleasantly—"This is a teetotal household: no strong drink of any kind is allowed to enter it. Will you have soda water or Appolinaris?"

Of course there was nothing to be said by a guest on the subject; but his host, like so many people professing his principles, had a good deal to say respecting the virtue of teetotalism. But so far as I was able to gather from the tone of his narrative, he did not obtain the cordial concurrence of his guest in all his views; for his guest was in the habit of taking half a bottle of claret at his dinner every day of his life and at least one glass of sound port afterwards, and for twenty years he had not gone to bed without wrapping himself round a tumbler of grog at the eleventh hour, and he did not find that an exordium on teetotalism went far to compensate him for the absent decanters. He was ready to greet the discourse with hisses; but the syphons were accommodating: they did their own hissing.

He went to bed in a very bad humour.

In the morning, however, after family prayers, his host said to him—

"I thought I detected an unsatisfied look on your face as you entered the room, my friend. I think I know the reason of it. I dare say you have been accustomed to something which you failed to find on the table in your room. I am sure of it. I have inquired, and I am very sorry for the omission. But make your mind easy; look on your table to-night, and I think you will be satisfied."

This was not so bad, the visitor thought; though not everything, still a whisky and soda going to bed was better than nothing.

He had his customary claret at his lunch in the pavilion that day, so he did not mind the sibilant but unsatisfying syphons at dinner. But he felt tired that night, he said, and went oft early to bed.

Switching on the light, he hurried to the table for the promised treat.

He found that the table bore nothing except a large Bible, bound in leather!

CHAPTER SIXTEEN—ART & THE ARTFUL IN THE PROVINCES

I.   —THE ARTISTIC OUTLOOK

A GOOD MANY PEOPLE ARE OF THE opinion that Art and the appreciation of Art are making considerable progress in this country, but others are inclined to be despondent on this subject; and among the most despondent is an estimable clergyman of a parish some miles from Broadminster. He told me that he was confirmed in his pessimism by observing the popularity of the imitation half-timbered, red-brick cottages which country architects are running up by the hundred in every direction. "The foundation of all true Art is Truth," he said, "and yet we are confronted daily with all the falsehood of creosoted laths curving about ridiculous gables in imitation of the old oak timbering. People hold up their hands in horror at the recollection of the outside stucco of the early Victorians; but where is the difference between the immorality of pretending that bricks are stone and of pretending that creosoted laths are old timbers?"

Of course he had many other instances of the inefficiency of the Schools of Art to fulfil the object of their establishment: there was the villa fireplace, for example, suggesting that its delicate ornamentation was of the fine paste of Robert Adam, when it was simply a horrible thing of cast iron; and what about the prevailing fashion in ladies' dress?...

It was time, he thought, that steps were taken by men of genuine artistic feeling to put people on the right track in regard to Art in daily life; and he expressed to me in confidence the belief that a change could best be brought about by an appeal to the sense of beauty inherent in womankind. He begged the co-operation of one of the Minor Canons at the Cathedral at Broadminster, who had achieved fame on account of his artistic tendencies, and this gentleman consented to deliver an address at a specially convened mothers' meeting in the parish-room of the reformer.

He kept his promise, as every one knew he would. He delivered an address on "The Influence of Cimabue on the later works of Donatello" in the presence of forty-two matrons, nearly all of whom could both read and write; and it was understood that he proved up to the hilt every statement that he made, and any of his audience who may have had some doubt as to the part that Cimabue played in the development of the genius of Donatello must have left the hall feeling that they could no longer hesitate in accepting the relative position of the two artists as defined by the lecturer.

The next address is, I hear, to be made on the subject of "The Cinquecento and its Sequel."

That is the way to popularise Art in the country districts. When once the wives and mothers of the farm labourers and the shepherds of the Downs are brought to understand the importance of taking a right view of Cimabue and the Cinquecento, then Art will become a living thing in this country—perhaps even sooner: who can tell?

Equally practical was the response made by a wealthy gentleman who has recently settled near Brindlington to the appeal of the parson to contribute something to the loan collection with which he hoped to second the efforts of the Minor Canon to stimulate an appreciation of good art in his parish. In charge of a traction-engine of large horse-power there was brought in a stone-mason's lorry to the door of the hall a full-size powerful group by Monsieur Rodin, representing an episode in the life of the most flagrantly humorous faun that ever grew, or half-grew, out of a rock under the rough-hewing chisel of the great French artist. At first one did not know that one was looking at a piece of sculpture—one seemed to be looking into a stone quarry. But gradually the idea revealed itself, and then one rather wished that it hadn't. The faun was not one of Nature's gentlemen: you could see that at once; but after a while, with good luck, you became aware of the fact that there was a nymph, or what looked like a nymph, scattered about the quarry—yes, you could see it quite distinctly from certain standpoints, and when you did you rather hoped that you had been mistaken. It was a masterpiece that "Group by M. Rodin." It might have been taken for a freak of Nature herself—one of those fantastic rocks which are supposed to suggest the head of the first Napoleon or perhaps the Duke of Wellington wearing his cocked hat, or it may be a huge lizard or, if properly humped, a kneeling camel. But whatever it was, there stood the stone quarry brought to the very doors of the hall wherein were "loaned" all the objects of Art contributed by the less ambitious collectors of the neighbourhood, and within were six stalwart men preparing to rig up on a tripod of fifteen-feet ash poles each as thick as a stout tree, a tackle of chains and pulleys for shifting the thing from the truck to the rollers by which it was to be coaxed into the building.

They did not get it beyond the porch. The tiled pavement crumbled beneath it like glass, and the caretaker of the building was doubtful about the stability of the floor within. In the porch it remained until the parson's wife, who had heard the noise of the traction-engine and felt sure that something was going on, arrived upon the scene.

She took a glance at the landscape within the porch, and then ordered a dust-sheet.

Of course the "Group by M. Rodin" was worth more than all the loans within the building; but it was not everybody's group. It remained in the friendly obscurity of the dust-sheet except when some visitor with inquisitive tendencies begged for a glimpse of it. Then the parson, averting his eyes, lifted up a corner of the dust-sheet, and remarked that he was sure that the work would be a noble one when the great sculptor should have cut away all the superfluous stone that lay in great masses about the figures; but even in its unfinished condition anyone could see that it could not weigh much under five or six tons.

I fancy that the gentleman who had contributed this loan was more of a humorist than the parson had suspected.

What I think is the most disappointing feature in connection with the development of Art in the provinces is the lack of interest shown in certain districts in the local productions. The producers are not without honour save in their own county. Of course, if it became a question of saving money, there would be patrons enough of local art; but unhappily the possible patrons are incapable of estimating correctly the money value of such things, and they prefer to give five pounds for a picture by an artist a distance than two for one by a local man, even though they might be assured by some one capable of pronouncing an opinion that the cheaper work was the better.

A few years ago I was made aware of a curious example of this characteristic of some places. It occurred to an enterprising printseller at Broadminster that a spring exhibition of works in black and white might attract attention and enable him to do some business; and with the co-operation of some of the London publishers he managed to get together over two hundred capital examples of modern work, including some proof etchings by Le Rat, David Law, Frank Short, Legros, and others. A local lady, who was understood to be a liberal and well-informed patroness of Art in various forms, visited the exhibition and was greatly attracted by an etching of a spring landscape. Finding the price moderate, she bought it and carried it home with her in her brougham. A week later, however, she returned with it to the printseller.

"Is it true that the Cuthbert Tremaine who did this is only a local man?" she inquired.

The printseller assured her that she was quite right: Cuthbert Tremaine's people belonged to the town, and he had been educated at the Grammar School and the School of Art.

"Do you think it was quite fair of you to hang that from such a person among the etchings that co-exibit here?" she asked.

"He was quite able to hold his own among the best of them," said the printseller. "He's coming well to the front, I assure you."

"I don't think that it is at all fair to your customers to try and foist off upon them the work of a local man," said the lady severely. "An ordinary local man! I wonder very much at your doing such a thing. I have brought the etching back to you, and you must change it for me. You really should have told me that Cuthbert Tremaine was nothing but a local man."

So much for the encouragement of local talent in our county.

Quite recently a more striking instance of this peculiarity was offered us in a neighbouring town. A local artist held a sale exhibition of water-colour drawings of scenes within a radius of six miles. There were perhaps thirty of these, and every one of them was good, and every one of them was pleasing. There was no suggestion of slovenliness about any, nor was there a hint of an amateur. They were not the sort of drawings that might be referred to as "highly creditable"—nobody wants to possess "highly creditable" things: they must have positive merit, without taking into consideration the conditions under which they are done, before any one who knows something about art would wish to possess them; and the watercolours in this exhibition could certainly claim to be in this light.

Well, cards of invitation were sent to some hundreds of possible buyers, and were heartily responded to, for free exhibitions are very popular in our neighbourhood, especially those that take the form of a demonstration of a new breakfast cereal (with samples gratis). But in the matter of sales the response was not quite so hearty as it might have been. The artist did not clear five pounds during the fortnight that his exhibition remained open.

A month or two later, however, a stranger exhibited a collection of his drawings in the same town, and although they were infinitely inferior in almost every way to those of the local man, they found quite a satisfactory number of purchasers, notwithstanding the fact that there was not a drawing that was not priced at more than double the sum asked by the local artist for his sketches.

II.   —ART AND THE SHERIFF

But before the end of the summer an opportunity was given to connoisseurs in the same town to acquire, at the expenditure of a few pounds, a collection of pictures that would do credit to any private gallery in the kingdom.
Announcements appeared placarded on every dead wall that "by order of the Sheriff" a magnificent collection of paintings by Turner, Reynolds, Gainsborough, Lawrence, George Morland, David Cox, and numerous other Masters, as well as drawings by Birket Foster, Keeley Hallswelle, George Cattermole, and a host of others. Being a Sheriff's sale this superb collection was to be disposed of without reserve, and the pictures were to be on view in the spacious commercial-room of an hotel.

People flocked to the place where these treasures were hung, and as a knowledge of pictures is born with most people, they were not slow to appreciate the fact that at last a chance had come to acquire at a merely nominal cost pictures by artists of world-wide fame. Most persons had read of the enormous prices brought by some prints after pictures by George Morland, but here were the actual pictures themselves in frames of the finest Dutch metal: no frames protected the high-priced prints in Christie's! And not merely was Morland highly represented here, but quite half a dozen exquisite *genre* pictures by Josef Israels were to be seen in a row, and it was whispered among the cognoscenti that this painter had just died and the *Studio* had contained an eulogistic article, with illustrations, on his work! Another chance! Of course Sidney Cooper's "Cows in Canterbury Meadows" spoke for itself. Every tyro knew that no one could ever paint cattle like Sidney Cooper. And Birket Foster—no one could ever approach Birket Foster in showing children swinging on a gate. There was the gate, sure enough, and the children, and the pet lamb—all the genuine Birket Foster properties. And "by order of the Sheriff."

It was a treat to see the *cognoscenti* examining the pictures, subjecting individual works to the severest tests of light and magnifying glasses, and then whispering gravely together in corners on the subject of their merits. Some of them had pencils, which they had pressed to their lips while they scrutinised the masterpieces, preparatory to making notes on their catalogues —all just like a London picture sale in King Street, St. James's Street, London, W.

And then some fool came into the room and laughed. He was a man who pretended to know a lot about pictures, and he was usually disposed to question the authenticity of things in the possession of everybody but himself. He glanced around the walls and went away, still laughing, after being in the place no longer than three minutes.

That was a trick on his part, the *cognoscenti* said. He wished to put them off buying and so make a haul for himself.

They were confirmed in this belief when the one dealer in the town told a gentleman, who had come to him with a commission to purchase some of the pictures, that the man had just been to caution him against buying any of them on his own account.

"He said that they are being hawked round from town to town, and that they are really all fakes—that there is not a genuine picture among the lot, and that the Sheriff's sale is not a *bona fide* one, but one of the oldest tricks of picture fakers."

But the knowing person said to the dealer—"Does he mean to say that in a town like this any man would dare to put 'by order of the Sheriff' at the top of the bill if it was not *bona fide?*He would pretty soon find himself in trouble. You attend the auction and bid for the numbers that I have marked in the catalogue."

The auction came off and was largely attended by the public, but, strange to say, by not a single outside dealer, only by the local one who had received many commissions. And a fortnight before an ordinary sale at a private house in the town, at which half a dozen pictures by fourth-class artists, and some only "attributed to" these artists, drew dealers from places fifty and sixty miles away!

It seemed pretty clear that the Sheriff had not taken a great deal of trouble to advertise this particular sale—he could not have given it his personal attention, or perhaps he had never before had a chance of handling the "fine arts" on so opulent a scale, or the dealers would certainly not have missed the chance of their lives.

However this may be, the pictures were bought by the dozen, as much as six pounds being given for each of the Israels, and a pair of Birket Foster's fetching ten, frames included in all cases. There was a keen struggle for the Turner, and it was run up to nine pounds—not by any means too much for a Turner as things go nowadays. Altogether, I suppose, about fifty pictures were sold. At the evening sale the auctioneer announced that a sufficient number had been disposed of to satisfy the Sheriffs claim, but that a gentleman in the trade had bought the remainder *en bloc*, and instructed him to put them all up for sale to the highest bidder; and he would have great pleasure in carrying out his instructions. On went the bidding down to the last lot, and so ended a memorable picture sale—probably the last of the kind to be perpetrated in England, for within a fortnight the gentlemen under whose direction the enterprise had been carried on from place to place for several years were arrested, tried, and convicted of perjury in making an affidavit with intent to deceive the Sheriff of some county and cause him to issue his writ for the sale of their bogus pictures. Fifteen months' imprisonment was certainly not too long a sentence for these practitioners; though really one can have but little sympathy for people who are such fools as to expect to buy pictures, with a name value of thousands of pounds, for a few shillings.

But for several weeks after the sale the fortunate purchasers of the bogus masterpieces lost no opportunity of exhibiting their treasures. Teas and At Homes were given to enable their less alert friends to. appreciate their varied charms, for it was understood in the town that the educational value of great works of art should not be neglected; and at the Mayor's Reception a short time afterwards two of the pictures were exhibited, for the educational benefit of the company, in their original Dutch-metal frames—the sort that one may buy for half a crown in a cash chemist's. In these days the man who had laughed at the private view was referred to in accents of scorn. But he continued to laugh, even when in the most kindly spirit he was advised by one of the successful bidders to remember that it was distinctly slanderous to suggest that a sale conducted under the auspices of the Sheriff of the county was a bogus affair. Then it was that the critic laughed loudest; and, so far as I can gather, he is laughing still.

One interesting point was brought out at the trial of the men. It was in respect of the actual manufacturer's price of the fraudulent pictures. The artist who had executed them was put into the box and stated that he received from five to fifteen shillings for each. The average trade price of a George Morland worked out at a fraction over seven shillings, so that to refer to these works as valueless would be wrong: those purchasers who were fortunate enough to secure good specimens of George Morland at the sale have the satisfaction of dwelling upon their varied beauties and reflecting that the actual value of each work is in the bogus market something between seven shillings and seven and twopence! (The "Sheriffs Sale" price of a Morland was six pounds.)

III.   —THE COUNTRY PICTURE SALE

I was once present at a picture sale in a mansion some miles from a country town in which I lived. There were, I think, three full-length Gainsboroughs, five Reynoldses, a few Hoppners, two by Peters, and three or four by Northcote. I was standing in front of a man by the first-named painter, and was lost in admiration of the firm way in which the figure was placed on the floor in the picture, when a local dealer approached me, saying—

"Might I have a word with you, sir?"

Of course I told him to talk away. I knew the man very well. He was one of those useful dealers of the variety known as "general," from whom one may occasionally buy a Spode plate worth ten shillings for three, or an odd ormolu mount for sixpence.

"We want to know if you believe these to be genuine pictures, sir," said he.

"Genuine pictures!" I repeated, being rather puzzled to know just what he meant; but then I remembered that he was accustomed to attend sales where pictures labelled "Reynolds," "Gainsborough," "Murillo," "Moroni," and so forth were sold for whatever they might fetch—usually from fifteen shillings to a pound, the word "genuine" never being so much as breathed by anyone. When I recollected this I laughed and said—"Make your mind easy. If these are not genuine pictures you will never see any come under the hammer."

"And what do you think they will fetch?" he inquired.

"I could not give you the slightest idea," I replied; "but if you can get me that one in front of us for five hundred pounds I'll give you twenty-five per cent, commission."

He was staggered.

"Five hundred!" he cried. "You must be joking, sir."

"I admit it," said I. "I should have said a thousand."

"But really, sir, how far would we be safe to go for them all? There are four of us here, and we are ready to make a dash for them if we had your opinion about them."

"Look here, my good man," said I. "You may reckon on my giving you five hundred pounds for any picture in this room that is knocked down to you. I'll put that in writing for you if you wish."

"It's not necessary, sir," he repeated. "We'll buy the lot of them for you for less money."

"Do, and I shall be a rich man afterwards," said I.

He went away chuckling.

The next day the auctioneer, who was an Irishman, after disposing of several lots of ordinary things, reached the pictures.

"I needn't say anything about them," he remarked. "They speak for themselves: I think you'll all agree with me that there's not one of them that isn't a speaking likeness. What shall we say for this one—No. 137 in the catalogue, "Lady Betty————," by Sir Joshua Reynolds? Look at her, ladies and gentlemen, and tell me if you think there are many artists in this county who could do anything better than this—all hand painted, and guaranteed. What shall we say?"

"A pound," suggested my dealer quite boldly. The auctioneer turned a cold eye upon him for a moment, and then I saw that there was a twinkle on its glossy surface.

"Very well, sir," he said. "A pound is bid for the picture—twenty-five shillings, thirty shillings, thirty-five, two pounds—thank you, sir; we're getting on—two-ten; I'm obliged to you, ma'am—three pounds ten—three pounds ten—three pounds ten bid for the portrait of Lady Betty. Oh, ladies and gentlemen, wouldn't it be a shame if such a picture was to be knocked down for seventy shillings and it worth nearly as many pounds. Four pounds —thank you, sir. The bidding is against you, ma'am. Well, if there's no advance————"

It was my dealer who had made the last bid, and I must confess that for some seconds I actually fancied that I was to be placed in possession of a Reynolds for four pounds!

THE LOCAL DEALER

"Four pounds—going at four pounds," came the voice of the auctioneer. "If there's no advance—going at four pounds—going—for the last time—five hundred—six hundred—seven hundred—a thousand—fifteen hundred—two thousand—guineas—five hundred—guineas—three thousand—guineas— going for three thousand guineas, ladies and gentle-men, it's giving the picture away that I am; but still the times are bad. Going at three thousand guineas—going—going—Mr. Agnew."

The hammer fell, and everyone was laughing except the Irish auctioneer and my dealer.

"Perhaps our dashing friend will give me an advance of thirty shillings on the next lot—Ralph, first Earl of————," said the former, glancing toward the latter with an insinuating smile.

The latter forced his way toward the nearest door, leaving Lot 132 to be started by a London dealer at a thousand pounds.

My disappointed friend had never been at a great sale in his life, and he had certainly not suspected that the gentlemen wearing the silk hats were like himself, dealers—only on perhaps a somewhat more heroic scale.

IV.   —HUMOURS OF THE ROSTRUM

The humours of the auction-room deserve to be dealt with more fully than is in my power to treat them. Though an auctioneer's fun is sometimes a little forced, its aim being to keep his visitors in a good temper with him—for he knows that every time that he knocks something down to one person he hurts the feelings of the runner-up—still, now and again, something occurs to call for a witty comment, and occasionally a ludicrous incident may brighten up the monotonous reiteration of slowly increasing sums of money. I have heard that long ago most lords of the rostrum were what used to be called "characters," and got on the friendliest terms with the people on the floor. But now I fear that there is no time for such amenities, though I heard one of the profession say, announcing a new "lot"—"Hallo, what have we here? 'Lot 67 —Adams Bed.' Ladies and gentlemen, there's a genuine antiquity for you— Adam's Bed! I shouldn't wonder if the quilt was worked by Eve herself, though I believe she was better at aprons."

The auctioneer as a rule, however, hurries from lot to lot without wasting time referring to the charm of any one in particular. I cannot understand how they avoid doing so sometimes when a beautiful work of art is brought to the front.

But in the old days I believe that now and again a trick was resorted to with a view to arouse the interest of possible purchasers in the business of the day. I know of such a little comedy being played with a good deal of spirited action in an auction-room in a large town in the Midlands. An Irish dealer was in the habit of sending round from time to time as much stuff as a large furniture van would hold, to be offered for sale by auction. Of course he placed a reserve on every article, and if this figure was not reached in one town, he packed up the thing, to give it a chance in the next; so that within a few weeks he managed to get rid of a large number of things at quite remunerative prices. It so happened, however, that he wanted money badly when he reached the town where he began his operations, and he made a confidant of the auctioneer, who promised to do his best in regard to the goods. The articles were consequently displayed in the rooms, and a considerable number of people assembled before the auctioneer mounted the rostrum. The bidding was, however, very spiritless, and the first dozen lots were knocked down to imaginary buyers at imaginary figures; but just when the thirteenth lot was exhibited there appeared at the farther end of the room a rather excited figure.

"Stop the sale," he cried. "I'm not going to stand passively by while you give my goods away. I don't mind a reasonable sacrifice, but I'm not going to submit to such a massacre as has been going on here up to the present. Stop the sale!"

"Look you here, Mr. O'Shaughnessy," said the auctioneer. "Massacre or no massacre, I received instructions from you to sell your stuff without reserve, and sell it I will, whatever you may say."

"You'll do nothing of the sort, I tell you," cried the Irishman. "Come down from that reading-desk and don't continue to make a fool of me. I'm not going to see my things thrown away. You know what they are worth as well as I do, and yet you knock them down for a quarter their value!"

"Now, my good man, if you don't get out of this room I'll have to take stronger measures with you," said the auctioneer. "I know that the stuff is all that you say it is; but that's nothing to me: the highest bidder will get the best of it, whether he bids to half the value or a quarter the value for that matter. You are making a fool of yourself, Mr. O'Shaughnessy, but you won't make a fool of me. I'm here to sell, and sell I shall. Now sit down or leave the premises."

"I'll not sit down. I tell you I'll not——"

"Porter," cried the auctioneer, "turn that gentleman out, and if he won't go quietly call a policeman. You hear?"

A couple of stalwart porters approached the vendor, saying soothing words; but he refused to move, and they had to force him to the door. They did so, however, as tenderly as possible; though he kept on shouting, as he went reluctantly backward step by step, that the auctioneer was in a conspiracy to ruin him, allowing his goods to be taken away for nothing. At last he was in the street and the door was closed. "Ladies and gentlemen," said the auctioneer, "I must apologise for this scene. Such a thing never happened in my mart before, and I hope it will never happen again. But I know my position, and I've no intention of breaking faith with the public, whatever that man may do or say. I hope you'll excuse him; he is really the best judge of antiques I ever met, but when he gets a drop of drink there's no holding him in. Now, gentlemen, he'll not disturb us again, and with your leave I'll proceed with the sale. I'll do my duty by you, and I'll do my duty by him, whether he has insulted me or not. He maybe an excitable Irishman, but that's no reason why we shouldn't do our best for him. Fair play, ladies and gentlemen, fair play to everybody. We must not allow our prejudices to blind us. You know as well as I do that the stuff is the finest that has ever come to this town, though the vendor would be safer in the hands of the police than prowling about as he has been. Now where were we?—ah, Lot 13 —'Chippendale mirror, carved wood, gilt.' There's a work of art for you. Where did he get hold of such a thing, anyway? What shall we say for it?"

The thing started at a figure actually above the reserve price that Mr. O'Shaughnessy had placed upon it, and the bidding went on with a rush. The next lot—two ribbon-carved mahogany arm-chairs—seemed to be badly wanted by some one. They were knocked down at a figure twenty-five percent, beyond the reserve. So it was with everything else in the collection. Never had there been a more successful sale in the same rooms.

alt="327 " width="100%" />

So, at least, the auctioneer confessed to the vendor as they dined together that evening, and the auctioneer was in private life a truthful man, though not always so rigid in the rostrum.

V. THE ARTFUL AND GOLDSTEIN

Upon another occasion, in the same town, there was a dealer's sale at an auction mart, and it went off pretty well, though naturally a good many lots remained undisposed of at the close, for on every article there was a reserve price representing the profit to accrue to the vendor, with the auctioneer's usual ten per cent. One of the unsold pictures had attracted the attention of a gentleman who had bid as far as twelve pounds for it, and when the sale was over he remained in the mart waiting to see if it should be claimed by a dealer, so that he might have a chance of getting it at a slight advance.

But the auctioneer very frankly confided in him that it had not been sold: the vendor, unfortunately, knew a good deal about pictures and had put a pretty stiff reserve on it. At this moment a local dealer showed signs of being also attracted by the picture. He stood in front of it, and seemed to be assessing its value to the nearest penny. After a few moments he jerked his head to bring the auctioneer to his side, and with a word of apology to the possible purchaser the auctioneer went to the man.

They had a whispered conversation together, but every whisper was clearly audible to the layman.

"Look here," said the dealer, "you know that I bid up to eighteen pounds for that picture. Well, I'm willing to go to the length of twenty for it, if you're selling it privately."

"I'm sorry I can't oblige you, Mr. Goldstein," said the auctioneer. "You know as well as I do who the vendor is, and you know that he is as good a judge of a picture as any man living. You know that the picture is worth money."

"Now what's the good of talking to me like that?" said Mr. Goldstein. "I don't deny that the picture is a good one—one of the best you ever handled—but a man must live. I believe I have a customer for that thing, but I look to make a bit off it for myself, and I must have it cheap."

"And isn't twenty-five pounds cheap for such a work?" asked the auctioneer.

"I don't deny it," replied the dealer, "and that's just what I expect to get for it; but where do I come in in the transaction if I pay you that for it? Do you fancy I stick in auction-rooms all day by the doctor's orders? I'll give you twenty-three pounds for the picture, and if you can't let me have it for that you may burn it."

The auctioneer laughed and walked away without condescending to reply, and with a grimace of ill-humour Mr. Goldstein left the auction-room.

"Who is that person?" asked the would-be purchaser.

"His name is Goldstein," replied the auctioneer. "He's a picture dealer, and about as knowing as they are made. He has been nibbling at this ever since it was left with me. Of course he'll come back for it. He's no fool. He knows a good thing when he sees it."

The auctioneer strolled down the room to his office, leaving the gentleman to digest the information which he had given him.

Now the gentleman was quite an astute person, and it did not take him long to perceive that a picture that is worth twenty-three pounds to a dealer named Goldstein is certainly worth twenty-five to a layman, so the auctioneer was not surprised when he entered his office, saying—

"Did you say that twenty-five pounds was the reserve for that picture?"

"That's the vendor's reserve, sir."

"All right. I'll take it at that," said the gentleman.

"Very good, sir," said the auctioneer, and he smiled knowingly as he added, "I may tell you that Goldstein offered me twenty-three for it just now. He'll be back with me offering twenty-five within the hour. I can imagine his face when he hears that it's gone."

His shrewdness did not deceive him. Mr. Goldstein was back at the mart within half an hour, with inquiries about the picture, and it was with an air of triumph that the auctioneer told him that it had been sold. It is also quite likely that the look which he said he would like to see on Mr. Goldstein's face when he heard that the picture was sold was exactly the one which was worn by Mr. Goldstein, though it might not be just the one which the purchaser of the picture would associate with an expression of chagrin on the face of a person named Goldstein.

The truth was that Mr. Goldstein was grinning quite pleasantly; for Mr. Goldstein was the vendor of the work of art, which he had bought for four pounds and had disposed of for twenty-five, less auction fees!

This auctioneer was an unusually clever man. He was heard to confide in a friend his impression that the town he lived in was not sufficiently large to give his genius a chance of being displayed to the full; and that was possibly why a short time afterwards he went to London and started business in one of the most central thoroughfares.

Within six months he was prosecuted for selling bogus Bechsteins, convicted, and sentenced to a term of imprisonment for an offence which at one time was a serious menace to the piano trade.

VI.   —TRICKS AND TRICKS

I have heard it debated with great seriousness whether a fine art dealer in a commercial town, where the finer arts are neglected, is not entitled to resort to a method of disposing of his goods which some people might be disposed to term trickery. Personally, I think any form of trickery having money for its object is indefensible. But there are tricks and tricks, and what will be chuckled over by some businessmen as "a good stroke of business" may, if submitted to a jury, be pronounced a fraud, and it appears to me that people are becoming more exacting every day in their fine art dealings. They seem to expect that a picture dealer will tell them all he knows about any picture that he offers them, and, should they consent to buy it, that he will let them have it at the price he paid for it. Should they find out, after they have completed the purchase, that he made any statement to them that was not strictly accurate, they bring an action against him. How such people would be laughed at if they were to bring an action against the vendor of a patent medicine for having stated on the bottle that it would cure gout, neuralgia, and neuritis, when they had tried it and found that it would do nothing of the sort! There was a pill made during the eighteenth century which was guaranteed to prevent earthquakes. Some time ago I heard it seriously urged, on behalf of an American patent medicine, that when the half of San Francisco had been laid in ruins by an earthquake, the building where the medicine was manufactured remained undisturbed!

But until recent years a pretty free hand was allowed to dealers in works of art. I remember being in a shop—called a gallery—in a provincial town in which a good deal of "restoration" in the picture way was effected. The proprietor had a drawerful of labels each bearing the name of a good old Master done in black on a gold ground, and when a work was "restored" to his satisfaction, he turned over the labels until he found one to suit its style. Then he nailed it very neatly on to the frame, and the picture was ready for sale as a Moroni, a Velasquez, a Tintoretto, or a Titian, as the case might be. The man was an excellent judge of pictures and prints, and I do not believe that he ever got a picture painted on an old canvas to sell as a genuine work. He simply bought all the good old pictures that he thought worth buying and "touched them up." People bought them on chance, the wise ones asking no questions "for conscience' sake"—the conscience of the vendor; and I am pretty sure that many genuine pictures passed through his hands—some that were worth from a hundred to five hundred pounds apiece for a tenth of the smaller sum.

He saw the humour of his labels better than anyone else, I think. He never gave an audible laugh when I used to inquire if he could provide me with a really choice Rembrandt for thirty shillings; he pretended to take me seriously, and, shaking his head, he would say—

"Rembrandts with any pedigree are getting scarcer and scarcer every year, sir. You wouldn't feel justified in going as far as two pounds if you saw one that you took a fancy to, I suppose? No? Well, I'll see what I can do for you at your price, but I may tell you that it's rather below than above the figure for a genuine hand-painted Rembrandt."

One day two gentlemen called when I was in the gallery—a major in the Gunners and a brother officer.

"Morning," said the former. "I hope you got the frame in order."

"Yes, sir," replied the dealer, bustling off to where a picture was lying with its face down on a bench. He picked it up and bore it to an easel, on which he placed it in a moderately good light. "That's it, sir. I happened to lay my hands on a more suitable frame, so I didn't trouble with the old one; it's impossible to put a touch of gold leaf on an old frame without making it look patchy."

"I think that's a far better frame than the old one," said the major. "I brought my friend in to look at the picture. Who did you say it was by?"

"Rubens, sir—an early Rubens, I think it is."

"Ah yes, that was the name. Looks well, doesn't it?" said the officer to his friend.

"Very well indeed. I never saw anything that took my fancy better," said the other. "Look at that silk—rippin', I call it—absolutely rippin'."

"I thought you'd like it," said the major. "There's nothing looks so well in a room as a good old picture. But, of course, it's easy overdoing that sort of thing."

"Nothing easier—like those American Johnnies," acquiesced his friend. "Yes, a rippin' picture, I call that—good colour, you know, but all well toned down. Do you know what it is—I've a great mind to have one too."

"Good!" cried the major. "You really couldn't do better, you know—six guineas, frame included."

"I believe you're right. Yes, I'll take one too," said the other, turning to the dealer, who was standing silently by.

"Very good, sir," said the dealer. "I'll look one out for you by to-morrow afternoon, if that would suit you."

"Suit me well. Six guineas in the frame, I suppose?"

"Yes, sir, six guineas, unless—— Would you like a pair of them, sir? I might be able to take a little off for a pair."

The grave way in which he suggested a pair of Rubenses, as if it were customary to sell Rubenses in braces like pheasants, was too much for my nerves. I looked at my watch and made for the door, and I hope that I was well round the corner before I burst out.

I heard afterwards that the officer had no use for a brace of Rubenses; but he bought a nice little Dutch village scene, by a painter named Teniers, for three pounds. It was not signed by the artist; but I have no doubt, if he had made a point of it, the dealer would have obliged him: the work of restoration frequently includes the restoring of an artist's signature.

So it was impressed on me that there is a humorous side even to picture dealing in the provinces.

That incident, I repeat, took place in the good old days; but if one gives some attention to the law courts even nowadays one will find plenty to laugh at in connection with transactions in the fine arts. It was certainly very amusing to see some year or two ago, the examples of fine old Dresden which were displayed as "exhibits"—in the legal, not the exhibition, sense—in the law courts, all of which were pronounced spurious by the experts, though sold for many thousand pounds to a wealthy old tradesman, and to follow the story of every transaction. But I found it more amusing still to identify the various pieces with the illustrations contained in aback number of a leading magazine of art which had devoted several pages to a description of the magnificent Dresden collection of the old tradesman. What had been referred to as the gems of the cabinets were the very things that were produced in the Court as examples of the spurious!